NERVES AND MUSCLES

Robert Galambos, who has been chief of the Department of Neurophysiology of the Walter Reed Army Institute of Research, in Washington, D.C., since 1951, interrupted his career in the laboratory to obtain a medical degree and approaches his subject from the points of view of both clinical practice and basic research.

An Ohioan, born in Lorain in 1914, Dr. Galambos succumbed to the fascination of science in his senior year at Oberlin College, where he received an A.B. degree in 1935 and an M.A. degree in 1936. It was his plan to enter medical school immediately, but the economic perils of the Great Depression steered him into academic work, where he could earn nearly enough money to live on. He did his graduate work at Harvard University, which awarded him the A.M. degree in 1938 and Ph.D. degree in 1941, and was a teaching fellow there in physiology and later an instructor.

In 1943 Dr. Galambos fulfilled his ambition to attend medical school, entering the Rochester Medical School. He received his M.D. degree three years later and has seen no reason to regret the interruption of his career in research. "Medical training," he says, "gives point and direction to the efforts of many biological investigators, and this it certainly has done for me."

After his internship at Emory University Hospital, in Atlanta, Georgia, Dr. Galambos returned to Harvard University in 1947 as a research fellow in the Psycho-

Acoustical Laboratory and remained there until assuming his position at Walter Reed.

This is Dr. Galambos's first book, but his technical contributions to scientific journals compose a long list. He is a member of the American Academy of Science and the National Academy of Science.

Nerves
AND
Muscles

BY ROBERT GALAMBOS

Published by Anchor Books
Doubleday & Company, Inc.
Garden City, New York
1962

ILLUSTRATIONS BY R. PAUL LARKIN
TYPOGRAPHY BY SUSAN SIEN

Library of Congress Catalog Card Number 62–10797
Copyright © 1962 by
Educational Services Incorporated
All Rights Reserved
Printed in the United States of America
First Edition

THE SCIENCE STUDY SERIES

The Science Study Series offers to students and to the general public the writing of distinguished authors on the most stirring and fundamental topics of science, from the smallest known particles to the whole universe. Some of the books tell of the role of science in the world of man, his technology and civilization. Others are biographical in nature, telling the fascinating stories of the great discoverers and their discoveries. All the authors have been selected both for expertness in the fields they discuss and for ability to communicate their special knowledge and their own views in an interesting way. The primary purpose of these books is to provide a survey within the grasp of the young student or the layman. Many of the books, it is hoped, will encourage the reader to make his own investigations of natural phenomena.

The Series, which now offers topics in all the sciences and their applications, had its beginning in a project to revise the secondary schools' physics curriculum. At the Massachusetts Institute of Technology during 1956 a group of physicists, high school teachers, journalists, apparatus designers, film producers, and other specialists organized the Physical Science Study Committee, now operating as a part of Educational Services Incorporated, Watertown, Massachusetts. They pooled their knowledge and experience toward the design and creation of aids to the learning of physics. Initially their effort was supported by the National Science Foundation, which has continued to aid the program. The Ford Foundation, the Fund for the Advancement of Education, and the Alfred P. Sloan Foundation have also given support. The Committee has created a textbook, an extensive film series, a laboratory guide, especially designed apparatus, and a teacher's source book.

The Series is guided by a Board of Editors, consisting of Bruce F. Kingsbury, Managing Editor; John H. Durston, General Editor; Paul F. Brandwein, the Conservation Foundation and Harcourt, Brace & World, Inc.; Francis L. Friedman, Massachusetts Institute of Technology; Samuel A. Goudsmit, Brookhaven National Laboratory; Philippe LeCorbeiller, Harvard University, and Gerard Piel, *Scientific American*.

INTRODUCTION

Probably the most obvious characteristic of animals and people is that they are always doing something. We, for instance, work, think, read, and move around as long as we live. Even when we seem to do nothing at all, our hearts beat, and we breathe, think, and see. These things happen because our nerves and muscles work every moment of every day.

If you have ever stopped to ask what laws govern these never-ending activities of animals and men, you are in good company; intelligent people have wondered for centuries how the brain and muscles manage to work together to produce behavior. What are the biological laws that operate when one of us sees objects, hears sounds, gets hungry, or makes muscles work to move his body from one place to another? In the old days people figured it would forever be impossible to discover these laws; they believed that what went on in living things was too complex for mere mortals to understand. By now, however, the idea that the special rules operating for nerves and muscles are simple variants of the well-known laws all matter obeys has taken firm root. How this idea grew out of physical and chemical measurements on living tissue is to be the main topic of this book.

To anyone with plain common sense most biological

laws turn out to be fairly easy to understand. Every farmer who makes money fattening cows for market has a practical working knowledge of the fundamental law of conservation of energy. He feeds his cows all the food they will eat, cuts down on their exercise, and ends up with heavy fat animals that bring a good price. If instead of this he reduces their food—or energy—input and increases their energy output by making them run several miles a day, he gets tough, stringy animals nobody will buy. The farmer's rule of thumb, as well as elegant scientific proofs, will show that the law of conservation of energy holds for the whole body and for every separate part of it. Many published studies carefully compare the calories put out as heat and work with the calories of energy put in as food; the numbers exactly balance or else there is a change of body mass. But, however much trouble you take in the proof, you always end up with the conclusion that the same law holds in biology and in physics. Neither the scientist nor the farmer understands exactly how the body makes the law work, but there doesn't seem to be too much mystery involved.

There are still other points of contact between physical laws and biological ones, and we shall touch on several of them. Consider light and heat, two well-known classes of energy every physics textbook discusses. The eye manages somehow to convert light energy into nerve impulses—the coin of the realm of the nervous system—and the study of the biophysics of this process by several generations of biological scientists has given us a collection of splendid experiments rich in clever ideas and solid facts. And everybody knows that a hot object, when touched, leads to quick withdrawal—unless we choose to leave the finger there and endure the pain. What do we know about the biological laws at work in cases like these? As we shall see, the experimental facts show the body makes such responses possible through extraordinarily ingenious use of basic chemical and physical principles.

It turns out, furthermore, that the way organisms do this is often far more effective than any our engineers have yet been able to figure out. Some scientists actually expect, for instance, that further discoveries about what goes on in nerve and muscle will enable the engineers to build in a much smaller space far better computing and analyzing machines than the ones we now use for tracking satellites, predicting election results, and so on. In many respects such nonbiological machines cannot hold a candle to the biological ones in accuracy, efficiency, and compactness.

In order to uncover the secrets of nerve and muscle action, biologists have borrowed most of their tools from the physics laboratory, improved or modified them, and then put them to work on living tissues. Consequently, cathode-ray oscilloscopes along with vacuum tubes and transistorized amplifiers are today as much the trade-mark of a biological laboratory as the stethoscope used to be of the country doctor.

All this interest in electrical gadgets stems from the discovery, over a hundred years ago, that active nerves and muscles generate electrical currents. Ever since then, hundreds of scientists have been relentlessly probing for better and still better methods to detect, display, and study this *bioelectricity*. This book, in large part, is an account of their struggles.

CONTENTS

CONTENTS

NERVES AND MUSCLES

CHAPTER 1

WAVES OF THE HEART

The biophysics of nerve and muscle is more than the mass of abstract knowledge to come later in this book, though you will find this knowledge interesting, I hope, and in places perhaps even amusing. People use the biophysics of nerve and muscle every minute of every day to help save lives in some hospital or other. To prove this point, let us in imagination visit a modern hospital and look around.

We enter not through the front door as an ordinary visitor would, nor via the emergency entrance like a patient rushed there in an ambulance. We go in through the side door, so to speak—the entrance used by the technicians and scientists who run its laboratories. These are the people who measure some response the sick person makes and compare it with what a healthy response would be. They earn their livings by providing physicians with the laboratory information that makes scientific diagnosis and treatment possible. Modern medicine demands many such scientific measurements on the patient—chemical, biological, physical—and so we could visit a good many different laboratories in our hypothetical hospital. Our specific interest in *biophysics* directs our attention, however, to those laboratories where biology and physics are so wedded that it is difficult to establish exactly where one ends and where the other begins. Biophysics—half biology, half physics—finds most use where heart disease and brain disorders come under the scientific eye. There are separate heart labs and brain labs. We shall visit the heart lab first.

The space set aside for the study of electrical waves generated by beating hearts actually looks more like an office than a laboratory. In it people seated at desks carefully examine narrow strips of paper. One of them reaches for a book, opens it and carefully compares what he sees on the strip before him with similar strips pictured in the book. Finally, satisfied, he puts the book away, turns to a typewriter and writes.

Electrocardiographic report [he writes it "EKG report"] on Patient Soandso. Routine electrocardiograms made on this 19-year-old man, admitted to the hospital in deep coma, show absent P-waves, depression of the S-T segment, and irregular ventricular rate. These findings could occur with marked elevation of blood-potassium level due to severe kidney disease. Details of the EKG findings follow. . . .

What follows takes several minutes. Finished at last, he looks toward us with a smile, and asks what we want. Before we can answer, the telephone rings. He picks up the instrument, listens, says a few words, and hangs up.

"That was the emergency room," he says, rising from his chair. "They have a man just brought in unconscious by an ambulance. The intern wants some EKGs on him. Would you like to come along while I take them?" We accept his invitation and follow along as he (or she) rolls a machine about the size of a portable TV out of a corner and wheels it through the hospital corridors. On the way he tells us that the intern suspects a heart attack but is not sure.

When we get to the emergency room, we find a man of perhaps 50 lying in bed. His skin is not pink but ashen-gray in color, and his pulse is barely perceptible at the wrist. Obviously, he is very ill indeed.

Our guide attaches metal plates about an inch square to the patient's wrist and ankle. Wires from each plate stretch to the EKG machine, which he turns on by flipping a switch. A narrow strip of paper starts rolling steadily like ticker tape out of a slot in the end of the instrument; on it is written a wiggling line which he and the intern inspect. Our guide tears off a short strip, carries it to a desk where the light is good, and examines it with great care. What is he doing, and what is this all about?

Well, in the first place, he knows that the normal heart, when it beats, generates electrical waves that spread throughout the body and can easily be picked up through electrodes on the wrist and ankle. He also is thoroughly familiar with the series of wiggling electrical waves the normal heart puts out, for as a medical student he spent many hours studying records taken on himself and his fellows. Finally, knowing what the normal record should be, he is searching through the

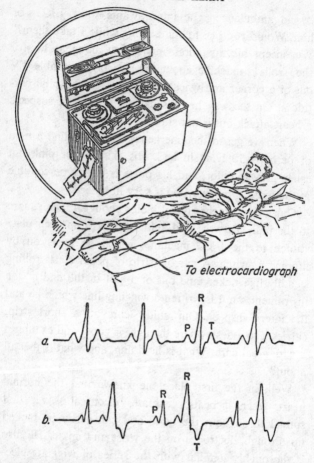

To electrocardiograph

Fig. 1. Wires attached to left ankle and right wrist carry
the heart's electrical activity to an EKG machine. Record a is from a normal heart, b from a person with heart
disease.

squiggles for signs of abnormality that will identify the patient's condition.

In most instances a skilled person has little difficulty telling at once whether a given patient suffers from a heart disorder. Fig. 1 illustrates how even you, in a few minutes of study, can detect the difference between normal and very abnormal EKGs.

Notice in the upper record that a series of waves—labeled P, R, T—recurs four times. Each PRT complex of waves represents one normal heart beat. Now look at the lower record. Taken from an abnormally beating heart, its electrical waves certainly reflect this fact. Instead of the neat PRT complex denoting the normal beat, the sequence is PRRT, and, besides, the two Rs are of different size, and the T is upside down. Such differences have real meaning to the expert eye. Many things can go wrong with a complicated organ like the heart, and almost every one, however slight and subtle, shows up as a telltale change in the total electrical picture of the heart's action. Normal heart, normal PRT complex; abnormal heart, peculiar electrical complex—this is the basic idea on which the entire medical speciality of cardiology is based. And behind this speciality is the simple biophysical fact that a bundle of muscles collected together in the form of the heart behaves like a generator of electricity whenever it beats.

Our unconscious patient lies unaware that the secret of his troubles is being clearly written in the electrical record put out by his heart. His anxious family, standing by, hopes that the mysterious goings-on will soon end in his return to good health. The doctor, examining the record, reads the written story, recognizes the needed treatment, and prepares to prescribe what is required for the cure. Let us flash back in time to the first biophysical experiments that made such a medical miracle possible.

CHAPTER 2

GALVANI'S EXPERIMENTS
WITH FROGS

It is a curious fact that a group of experiments on frog legs has yielded supremely important discoveries for both physics and physiology. Out of them came electric batteries and X-ray machines and radio sets, and also brain waves, the laws of electricity and scientific diagnoses of human heart disease. Luigi Galvani and his gentle wife, Lucia, performed these revolutionary experiments in Italy during the 1780s, and here are two of them.

A Frog and Some Lightning

Experiment 1: The Galvanis took a dissected frog outdoors on an upstairs porch, attached a lightning rod to its head end, stretched another wire from its foot to the water in a well, and then sat back to wait for a storm to blow up (Fig. 2). Soon the summer sky darkened and, in Galvani's words,

as the lightning broke out, at the same moment all the muscles fell into violent and multiple contractions, so

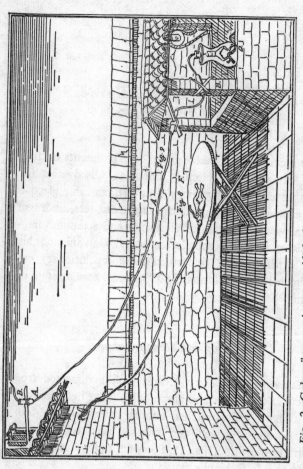

Fig. 2. Galvani's experiment, published in 1791. Wire from lightning rod (A, B) runs to head end of frog; wire from foot dips into the water in the well at the right.

that, just as does the splendor and flash of the lightning,
so too did the muscular motions and contractions . . .
precede the thunders, and, as it were, warn of them.

Doubtless we all can share the astonishment of the
guests who, invited out on the porch to see for themselves, watched the frog jerk and twitch every time a
distant lightning bolt flashed through the sky. A simple
explanation of what then must have seemed a miracle
comes easily today. During a thunderstorm the atmos-
phere becomes heavily charged with electricity and a
lightning flash occurs whenever a large amount of this
electrical charge approaches the ground.* The lightning
rod provides a path by which a small amount of this
charge may make contact with the earth. So the frog
Galvani wired into the lightning-rod circuit merely received and reacted to a modest electric current that
flowed through its body at the time a distant lightning
bolt fired off.

Galvani knew some of these facts very well, for Benjamin Franklin forty years earlier had invented the lightning rod for the express purpose of removing atmos-
pheric electricity in a harmless manner. What was
entirely new to Galvani and his friends was the fact that
an electric shock is a very good way to rouse nerves and
muscles into activity.

* See Louis J. Battan, *The Nature of Violent Storms*,
Science Study Series, Doubleday, 1961.

A Frog on a Railing

Experiment 2: This one also was performed outdoors, the dissected frogs being hung this time over an iron railing on bronze hooks pushed through the body between the shoulder blades. Whenever a leg of a frog chanced to touch the iron railing, it jerked away, and after a short convulsion the frog relaxed and its foot stretched out again. The moment the foot touched the iron railing once more, the spasm of contraction returned. This cycle of spasmodic jerking followed by relaxation recurred again and again, touched off in each case when some part of the frog made contact with the iron railing. Somehow, completing the circle frog to iron railing to bronze hook to frog meant that the frog would jump.

We now know that these frogs and the one in Experiment 1 jumped for the same reason: an electrical current passing through their bodies made them do it. At the point where the iron railing and bronze (an alloy of copper and tin) hook made contact, an electrical potential existed, and when the body of the frog bridged the gap between the two metals by touching the iron railing, a flow of current passed through the entire circuit. Neither Galvani nor anyone else at the time possessed a clear knowledge that dissimilar metals like iron and bronze in contact with one another are a potential source of electrical current. No one knew much at all about this or any other kind of battery. Yet his frogs jerked when a current flowed through them for exactly the same reason that modern frogs will jerk when we connect their bodies across the poles of a battery or dry cell.

Galvani's primitive iron-bronze battery, while not actually the first ever created, is nevertheless one of the outstanding discoveries of history. Galvani never realized its full significance, but his friend Volta did and promptly exploited it. Experimenting further with dissimilar metals, Volta finally created, around 1800, the first usable battery. By this time both Galvani and his wife had died.

Following on those early discoveries of the great Italians, the science of electricity has grown by leaps and bounds during the past 150 years. Conversion of the new knowledge into practical new devices kept pace. All those applications we know so well—street lights, electric toasters, television, and the countless other everyday devices run by electricity—were born, one can say, on that memorable day when Galvani hooked his frogs to an iron railing. However, if you want more information about the revolution in physics and good living set off by Galvani and Volta, you will have to look elsewhere since this book sticks closely to what goes on in nerves and muscles.

Actually, Galvani's experiments made at least as big a difference to biology as they did to physics. In the ten years following his original report Galvani's experiment was repeated over and over throughout Europe wherever frogs and dissimilar metals could be brought together, which is to say practically everywhere. "Dead" frogs were experimentally restored to "life" countless times, and fantastic stories were invented to explain the vital forces Galvani was supposed to have uncovered. Before long, however, scientific explanations also began to appear out of the intense activity he set into motion, and these boil down to the following rather simple facts of physics, chemistry, and biology.

1. Dissimilar metals like iron and copper, when brought into contact with each other in the proper way, can produce an electric current. This, of course, is the basic principle underlying all batteries.
2. Electricity flows through all conductors including substances like nerve, muscle, and the fluid that bathes them. The body of a frog or man carries electricity almost as well as a piece of copper wire.
3. An electrical current throws muscle and nerve into brisk activity closely resembling what they normally display. Galvani's lightning rod and battery experiments both proved the close tie-up between normal body processes and electrical events. An entirely new science, electrophysiology, arose out of this realization.

Portrait of an Electrophysiologist

Electrophysiology is a science having two main goals. Some of its practitioners—like the hypothetical doctor we left looking at the EKG of the hypothetical stricken patient—make close observations of the electricity manufactured by living tissues going about their normal activities. Others—like Galvani, the first electrophysiologist—study what happens when electric currents pass through living tissues and arouse responses in them. Both approaches—the study of electricity produced by living things, and the effects of electrical currents upon living things—have given valuable insights into life processes.

The electrophysiologists to whom these insights arrive make up an interesting breed of scientist. They come to their work with interests and training as rich and varied as the shapes and sizes of the animals they study. Some specialize on muscles rather than nerves, others the reverse. Some always work with people, never with animals; others feel at ease only when experimenting in the animal laboratory. Yet despite these wide differences in interest, their background training is likely to show very many common features.

For instance, all have a solid basic knowledge of body structure: one must know how nerves and muscles fit together in the body if he wishes to study intelligently how they work together. Hence anatomy, and especially the anatomy of the nervous system, comes high on every list. Next, the principles of physics, and in particular the laws of electricity; that *electro* in the word electrophysiology suggests by itself the importance of electrical theory and practice in the intellectual equipment physiologists bring to their work. Not every electrophysiologist is a qualified electrical engineer, but nearly any of them, in a pinch, could find out why a simple radio refused to play. The electrophysiologist must have at least a modest familiarity with the working principles of electronic devices, for in his laboratory he sees them wherever he looks. Several electrophysiologists have also been brilliant electronic engineers, making substantial contributions in both fields. They, however, have been the exceptions, not the rule.

Besides anatomy and physics, some knowledge of chemistry, of psychology, and of the processes going on in living things (physiology) is required, for the language of electrophysiology is a polyglot drawn from all these disciplines. Here is a typical example:

> Most bioelectric events in the nerve-muscle preparation result from breakdown and recovery of unstable physical-chemical membranes; movements of sodium and potassium ions are associated with excitation and the membrane collapse, while oxidative chemical reactions producing heat occur during the recovery following membrane restoration. The electrical events themselves, as recorded from single nerve and muscle cells through suitable high-gain amplifiers with a band pass of at least 30 kc, are polyphasic with a prominent early event lasting about 1 millisecond. Recordings taken simultaneously from many cells prove extremely useful for measuring minimum reflex times, as in the knee jerk, and in establishing reaction times in eye-hand, ear-foot, and similar behavioral responses. In clinical medicine the specialties of electroencephalography and electrocardiography draw heavily upon the basic information developed by electrophysiologists. Much, finally, of what we know about sensory processes such as vision and hearing and about the higher functions of the organism such as learning stems from their electrical measurements on sense organs, neurons, and muscle fibers.

Equipping you, the reader, with enough knowledge to make some sense out of that paragraph is the main goal of this book. If by now some of it already makes

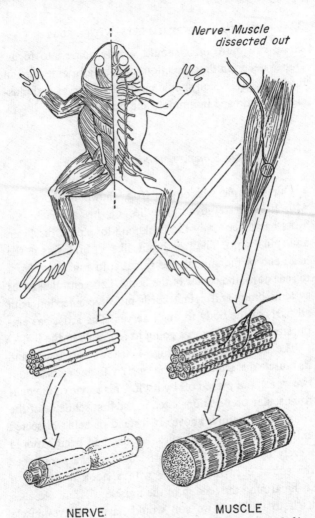

NERVE.   MUSCLE

Fig. 3. Dissected frog: Muscles uncovered in left half, central nervous system exposed in right half. Dissection of muscle and nerve to individual cells also shown as the cell would appear under microscope.

sense, still more of it should shortly come into focus. Our first step in that direction must be a brief excursion into anatomy, which should clarify how nerves and muscles are arranged in animals like ourselves.

Some Anatomical Facts

Our example will be the frog, shown in the Fig. 3 with its skin removed. He lies on his stomach; the artist has taken away the backbone to expose the brain and spinal cord. The frog brain, like all brains, is at the head end of the animal; the spinal cord runs from front to rear down the center of the body. This central nervous system—brain and spinal cord—makes connection with all parts of the body through nerves. The artist has emphasized one such nerve going to a muscle in the leg.

The next illustration (Fig. 4) shows this nerve and its muscle dissected out of the frog (with fine scissors and tweezers) and placed off by itself. This is one of the neuromuscular preparations cited in the first sentence of the complex paragraph above. If instead of being dissected entirely out of the frog, these tissues had been exposed merely by, say, lifting a short length of the nerve near the spinal cord into the air with a hook and tying a string around the tendon of the muscle where it attaches itself to the foot, we still would have a nerve-muscle preparation, but this time it would remain in its normal place in the body. Completely dissected and partly dissected nerve-muscle preparations both find much use in the laboratory.

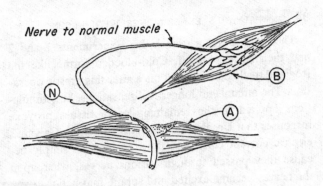

Nerve to normal muscle

N

B

A

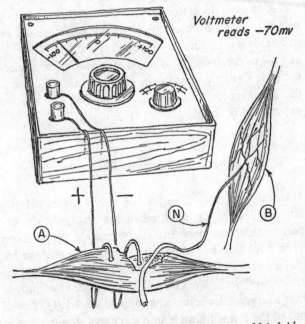

Voltmeter reads −70mv

+ −

A

N

B

Fig. 4. TOP: *Muscle* B *twitches when its nerve* N *is laid across the cut in muscle* A. BOTTOM: *Voltmeter shows sizable voltage difference between the cut and normal portions of muscle* A; *current is flowing across nerve* N.

The frogs Galvani used in his Experiments 1 and 2 had their heads cut off. Cold-blooded forms like the frog and turtle do not die at once after this drastic operation. The animals no longer feel sensations, but stimulations applied to the remaining nerve tissues provoke responses that closely resemble normal action. Galvani's electric current convulsed the frog muscles simply because they passed through various nerves, whereupon the nerves became excited and sprang into action. Anyone who has accidentally pushed his finger into a light socket doesn't have to be told that electricity causes nerves to react. Such electrical stimuli work equally on people, frogs, and nerve-muscle preparations. There is, as you might imagine, a single explanation why electricity is similarly effective in all these cases. To get at this common explanation, let us look at still another experiment on frogs.

Experiment 3: Animal Electricity

In this experiment, performed after Galvani's death, no wires, hooks, or other metals are involved. The experimenter used only two nerve-muscle preparations (Fig. 4). When he placed a frog nerve N against the cut surface of muscle (A), the normal muscle (B) began to twitch and jerk. To Galvani this would have proved that a mysterious something, animal electricity, flowed out of the injured muscle into the nerve that touched it and then ran on down to the second muscle, which jerked upon its arrival. What actually happens is both more simple and more complex than this, and the person who grasps what goes on will have a pretty good basic idea of why electrical currents rouse nerves and muscles into action.

Suppose, first of all, that we touch the cut muscle (A) with wires leading to a voltmeter instead of with the nerve Galvani used (Fig. 4). Our voltmeter will reveal whether an electrical potential exists between the two places we touch. This voltmeter, connected across an ordinary flashlight battery, would give a reading of 1.5 volts; when connected across either a normal region of the muscle or its cut surface, it would give a zero reading. But when connected as shown in the bottom figure, between the normal and cut surfaces, it reveals a potential difference of 70 millivolts (70 mv) existing between them. The cut surface is negative by 70 mv compared to the normal region, and this situation persists until the tissue dies completely. Here then is proof of a biological battery fully one-twentieth as strong as a flashlight battery.

This biological battery ought to be strong enough to produce a modest current flow, and there is not much question that it was indeed just such a current flow from normal to cut surfaces in muscle (A) that caused stimulation of the nerve lying upon it. The body fluids of a frog contain large amounts of sodium, chloride and other ions that conduct electricity readily. If muscle (A) is wet, as it is likely to be, this fluid will carry electrons between the cut and normal surfaces. A flow of electrons in one direction is exactly the same as a flow of current in the opposite direction. What the old-timers termed "animal electricity" generated in muscle (A) turns out, therefore, to be nothing but ordinary electrical current driven through tissue fluids by a biological battery, and thus the flow of an electric current through an excitable nerve explains still another of his spectacular experiments.

Let us digress a moment here to straighten out the terms electron-flow and current-flow. When Benjamin Franklin was studying electricity, it was the custom to say the electrical current (he thought of it as a kind of fluid) flows from positive to negative. He must have had in mind the analogy of water flowing from a higher point to a lower one. Long after Franklin died, a flow of current was shown actually to be a flow of negative charges, ions or electrons, moving in the opposite direction. Thus the two ideas, current-flow from positive to negative and electron-flow in the opposite direction, describe the same event. We shall talk mostly about the way the electrons or negatively charged ions flow.

In wires made of iron or copper, current flows because adjacent molecules of the metal "pass" electrons back and forth as if they were so many players in a basketball game. The atoms of the metal stay fixed in space while the electron "balls" move along from one atom to the next. In biological tissues, atoms do not remain fixed in place as they do in metallic wires, for the substances in and around cells are dissolved in water and therefore move about with reasonable ease. Many such dissolved particles are electrically neutral, but many others either carry an excess of electrons or suffer from a deficiency of them. Those with the excess are called negative ions, while those with the deficit are, of course, the positive ions.

If wires from the plus and minus poles of a battery are dipped into a solution containing a mixture of such biological ions, the negatively charged ones migrate away from the minus pole and stream toward the plus pole, where they deliver up their electrons and undergo a chemical change. During this migration they are jostled about by the stream of traffic moving in the reverse direction—the positive ions hurrying to the negative pole, where electrons are freely available. Thus current flowing in a biological system differs in several important ways from what goes on in a copper wire. In contrast to what happens in a wire, the negative ions actually carry electrons through the solution. This mobility of negative and positive ions, as well as their opposite properties, is a fact to which we will later return.

CHAPTER 3

THE MEMBRANE THEORY

Now let us give the biological battery Galvani discovered a somewhat closer look. Presumably you can imagine the 70 mv potential between the cut and normal surfaces of the nerve-muscle preparation (Fig. 4) and the busy traffic of negative and positive ions moving in opposite directions under its influence. What maintains this potential in the biological battery? Furthermore, why does a flow of ions crossing that nerve resting on muscle (A) rouse it into action? The key to the answer for both questions is a single explanatory concept—the so-called *membrane theory*. This theory is in its way comparable to the electron theory in physics; the electron theory "explains" much of what we know about the physical universe while the membrane theory similarly "explains" several fundamental properties of nerves and muscles.

Galvani did not know that his frog muscle actually was made up of thousands of long cylindrical cells called muscle fibers, bound together in a bundle. The true situation was not discovered until many years after his death. He did not realize, therefore, that the single structure he called "muscle" was in fact a collection of thousands of independent, separate, smaller structures, the muscle fibers, each like a kind of elongated amoeba with its own cell membrane. With proper equipment a patient person can dissect one such muscle fiber away from all its neighbors, put it in a dish by itself, and with a microscope watch it carry on a lively, independent existence. It contracts when you touch it, and in every way it displays in miniature the properties of the large muscle of which it was a part. A thin membrane forms the barrier between the outside world and the protoplasmic interior of the cell, where everything connected with its business—contraction or shortening—proceeds.

Membrane Potential

In each cell this membrane surrounds the gelatinous protoplasm as the skin surrounds a sausage. Physiologists have reason to believe that this sausage-casing of a membrane is electrically polarized. An excess of negative ions is collected on the inside of the membrane while a corresponding number of positive charges matches them on the outside. This arrangement of charges is stable in a cell at rest, and because of the arrangement the substantial 70 mv potential difference exists between the inside and the outside of such a cell. It makes no difference whether the cell comes from a plant, fish, or man; it may originally have been part of the liver or brain: so far as we know, every cell possesses a polarized membrane across which a measurable potential exists.

The polarized portion of the membrane of a cell has

never been seen, even with an electron microscope, and so, like the electron and the atom, it might be called a figment of scientific imagination. The biological membrane *may* exist just as atoms and electrons may exist; no one knows for sure. What we do know, however, is that nerve and muscle cells behave *as if* covered by polarized membranes, and if we suppose they are, we can readily explain many experimental results.

Obviously, the theory takes care of the 70 mv measured between cut and normal surfaces of muscle (*A*), for instance. Muscle (*A*) is actually thousands of individual biological batteries—muscle fibers—lined up in parallel. In dividing the muscle with a knife, one exposes the inside protoplasm of all the severed fibers. This cut surface should be negative with respect to a distant normal region since the voltmeter is connected across the inside and outside of the muscle cells—and it is.

The membrane theory also can explain what happens to the nerve draped across muscle (*A*) in Fig. 4. It becomes excited, you will recall, and according to the theory, this too makes good sense, as you can see in the following argument.

Like the muscle, every "nerve" such as the one here contains hundreds or even thousands of separate nerve fibers arranged in parallel (Fig. 3). The resting nerve fiber is again like each muscle fiber in possessing a membrane polarized so that a difference of 70 mv exists between its inside protoplasm and the outside fluid. By its very nature this polarized membrane cannot be completely stable. We conceive it to be, after all, simply a submicroscopic arrangement of charged ions and a delicately balanced one at that. Ions flowing in the vicinity might profoundly disturb this balance—and the current generated by cut muscle certainly sends many ions coursing across and among the nerve membranes. Indeed (so the theory goes) whenever this muscle-induced ion flow becomes sufficiently dense, it destroys the nerve membrane potential completely, and this is the first step in the excitation process observed. Excitation, then, equals membrane depolarization.

But how would such a complete destruction of the 70 mv potential in nerve fibers cause twitches in faraway muscle (B)? The theory explains this too—if we suppose that collapse of the membrane potential at one spot in a given nerve leads to its ultimate destruction everywhere. Just as the fuse in a firecracker burns its way from where the match is applied on down to the body of the firecracker, so for the nerve fibers in this experiment: collapse of their membrane potential at the point where they touch muscle (A) is followed by spontaneous and progressive destruction down the nerve in the direction of muscle (B). On arrival at muscle (B) this collapse of membrane potential sets into motion a series of processes—in which, incidentally, disappearance of the membrane potential in the separate fibers of muscle (B) is an important step—that end in the twitches and contractions that amazed and intrigued the scientists of Galvani's time.

One final point and this general description of the membrane theory will be complete. Experiments prove that when this membrane we have been visualizing collapses, it doesn't stay that way very long. In fact, the membrane no sooner has collapsed than it begins restoring itself to normal once more. This discharge and recharge of the biological battery can occur in a nerve of man (and cat as well) as often as several hundred times every second, the energy for recharging coming ultimately from the oxidative chemical events of the body cells.

Oxygen and Nerve Action

Nerves, like all other cells in the body, require oxygen to carry out their work. A simple experiment upon a nerve deprived of oxygen demonstrates this is so. Suppose a length of frog nerve is stretched out inside an airtight box having two compartments as shown in Fig. 5. Let us fill one compartment with oxygen, the other with nitrogen. Shortly after we do so, the section of nerve in the nitrogen compartment should significantly change its properties if it is true that nerves require oxygen to carry out their tasks.

Comparing the nerve membrane potentials in the two compartments shows the properties do change. At the beginning of the experiment no difference exists between the two nerve sites where the electrodes lie, as we already know. After some minutes, however, the nerve exposed to nitrogen stops being normal for, as the graph shows, a negative voltage-difference appears between it and the nerve in the oxygen compartment. This difference becomes larger with time, reaching many millivolts

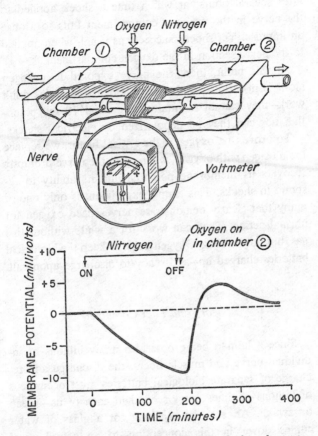

Fig. 5. Experiments like this one, described in the text, prove that nerves and muscles, like all living cells, require oxygen.

after several hours, at which time a shock applied to the nerve in the nitrogen compartment fails to arouse an impulse. Yet shocks succeed, as usual, when applied to the nerve section in the oxygen compartment.

At this point, then, the nerve exposed to nitrogen alone is in serious trouble. Its biological batteries don't work—they cannot maintain the normal 70 mv potential, nor can they be depolarized by electrical shocks.

To prove that oxygen is the critical factor, we replace the nitrogen with oxygen, whereupon the nerve promptly recovers its membrane potential and its ability to respond to shocks. This simple experiment is only one of many that clearly demonstrate nerves need oxygen for normal action. They can work for a while without this gas, but not for long. Oxygen helps to keep the biological batteries charged up—and ready to discharge upon call.

Theory and Fact Combined

Since a human being possesses many billions of individual nerve and muscle fibers, the discharge and recharge of separate biological batteries must occur tens of billions of times every second in each of us—asleep or awake. An act like reaching for a glass of water comes down—in this conception—to an astronomical number of nerve and muscle membranes depolarizing in a particular and specific orderly sequence. Kicking a football differs from reaching for the glass only in that another unique sequence of nerve and muscle batteries discharges and recharges. All our behavior, in fact, must be determined by the exact constellation of nerves and muscles engaging in this vast electrical game.

Perhaps Galvani would be shocked if he could know his experiments have generated such an idea as this. Yet it and many more like it derive directly from the two fundamental facts he discovered—that nerve and muscle cells generate electrical currents, and that flowing electrical currents can change the cells from an inactive to an active state. The generations of scientists who followed his lead—and indeed are still doing so—have turned up answers to several basic questions of which the following will serve as examples.

Just how fast do the nerves conduct their impulses? Hermann von Helmholtz, the German genius, was the first to solve this puzzle. His success must have embarrassed his teacher, Johannes Müller, who only a few years earlier had rashly predicted that no one would ever manage to measure the speed of nerve impulses. What Helmholtz did in a famous experiment in 1848 was to cause a frog muscle to contract by applying electric shocks to its nerve at two different distances from the muscle. He measured the time interval between nerve shock and muscle contraction when he shocked the nerve 1 cm from the muscle and compared this to the time interval noted when he shocked 5 cm from the muscle. There was a difference of about .0013 sec between the two measurements, and this time was obviously consumed as the nerve impulses traveled over the 4 cm length of nerve.

From this information he figured out (and so can you) that the impulse travels down frog nerve at a rate very close to 30 meters per second. That's about 65 miles per hour, a good, fast rate for a lowly frog. Since Helmholtz's day conduction velocities in nerve from many different animals have been accurately determined and the following generalizations seem always to hold.

1. The larger the diameter of the nerve fiber the faster the impulse travels in it. Tiny fibers 1 micron across conduct at perhaps 1 meter per sec while large ones 15 or 20 microns across conduct at 100 meters per sec or better. This 100 to 1 difference in velocities occurs in bodies like our own, for we possess nerve fibers of all sizes.

2. Conduction velocity depends very much upon temperature—the higher its temperature the more rapidly a given nerve carries its message. For most nerves the relationship is simple and linear over a range of at least 10° Centigrade, the rate being approximately doubled by the 10° rise. For organisms like ourselves, in which body temperature remains nearly constant day and night throughout the year, this fact probably has little significance. But for animals like snakes, frogs, and fish, body temperature depends upon outside temperature and so part of their sluggishness and inactivity in winter can undoubtedly be explained by a slowing down of activity in their neurons.

Is the nerve message constant in size or does it vary? Biologists once thought that the amount of message a nerve fiber carries might vary in size, being small at one time and large later on. Like a garden hose, the nerve fiber was supposed to carry a trickle or a torrent. Old-time physiologists also thought of each muscle fiber as shortening a small, medium, or large amount, depending on what the body needed. About 50 years ago, however, physiologists began to collect experimental evidence for exactly the opposite view, which holds that each nerve and muscle fiber has only two states—full activity or complete rest.

According to this idea, the amount of response a cell produces is essentially independent of the size of the stimulus exciting it. Strong stimuli will not provoke a larger response from it than weak ones because every cell, however activated, exerts itself to the maximum of its capacity. Furthermore, after its exertion the cell quickly sinks back into a resting state only to be once again roused to its fullest activity on arrival of another proper stimulus.

This idea of nerve and muscle cells alternating between two extremes, rest on the one hand and full activity on the other, has been tested and verified in many different kinds of experiments. Perhaps the demonstration by Kato gives the most simple and direct proof.

This Japanese physiologist laboriously cut away all the nerve fibers except one in a toad nerve-muscle preparation. Such a single nerve fiber makes connection with (innervates) only a very few muscle fibers, and these will contract, of course, whenever the nerve delivers its message to them (Fig. 6). Kato showed that the twitches given by such muscle fibers remained constant in size no matter how strongly he stimulated the nerve. Since his weak shocks as well as his strong ones all yielded the same amount of muscle action, he concluded that no intermediate stage between complete rest and

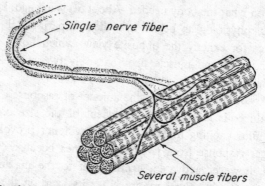

Fig. 6. *Nerve fiber emerging from brain or spinal cord ends upon many muscle fibers—7 in this illustration.*

fullest exertion was possible for either the nerve or the muscle fibers in the preparation.

Our membrane theory predicts this result, as indeed it must if we are to take it at all seriously. As you will recall, the theory in the form we now know it says total collapse and disappearance of the 70 mv membrane potential is the fundamental phenomenon in active nerve and muscle fibers. Unless the membrane potential has collapsed, the cell is at rest, and when the membrane potential has disappeared, the cell is fully active. There is no intermediate stage.

The Idea of the "Threshold" Stimulus

Suppose we consider the amount of current Kato used to stimulate his single nerve fiber. His "shock" creates a flow of electrons traversing the nerve, and this flow

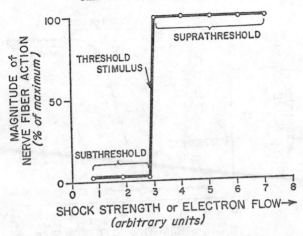

Fig. 7. Graph showing results of shocking a single nerve. Nerve action (ordinate) is measured by the amount of muscle action produced. Nerve is either fully active (suprathreshold) or wholly inactive (subthreshold), and the transition between these two states is abrupt (threshold).

can be experimentally regulated to be small or large as we choose. Too few electrons flowing will fail to produce nerve-membrane potential collapse and the nerve will not become active. Electron-flows above a certain amount, however, will all be successful, and equally so.

Physiologists give to the smallest successful quantity of electrons a special name, the *threshold* quantity. Fewer than this amount produce only subtle changes in the membrane (which we will go into later). These ineffective stimuli are, then, *subthreshold*. Quantities larger than the threshold amount—*suprathreshold* quan-

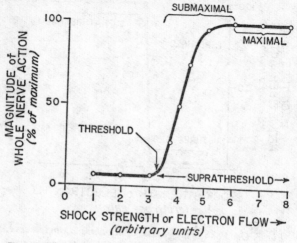

Fig. 8. *Graph showing results of shocks to a bundle of nerve fibers. Again the ordinate (nerve action) is estimated by measuring muscle response. Since all nerves in the bundle do not have the same threshold, the abrupt transition seen in Fig. 7 does not appear here.*

tities—invariably produce nerve-membrane potential collapse and excitation.

Thus when we apply gradually increasing quantities of electrical stimulation to a nerve fiber it reacts in a predictably nonlinear manner. At first it is apparently unperturbed by our weak subthreshold shocks, but when we reach threshold strength, it springs into full and complete activity. Suprathreshold shocks turn out to be no more effective than the threshold ones, unless, of course, they are made so intense they cook the tissue. Fig. 7 shows this chain of events in graphic form.

While every one of the hundreds of fibers collected together in a nerve obeys these threshold rules, for various reasons the threshold shock strength is not the same for them all. Some fibers—perhaps because their location on the outside of the nerve-cable makes them more easily accessible to the flow of stimulating current—respond to shocks weaker than others need. Shocks that are suprathreshold for some fibers can therefore still be subthreshold for others.

This somewhat complicates things, but it was arbitrarily decided long ago to consider the threshold of the most sensitive fiber to be the threshold for the entire group. Fig. 8 shows how such a collection of nerve fibers would react for ready comparison with the way a single fiber responds. The new terms *submaximal* and *maximal* identify two classes of suprathreshold stimuli peculiar to the whole nerve preparations; their properties find interesting uses in advanced research on nerve and muscle.

CHAPTER 4

BASIS OF BIOELECTRICITY

Wherever they look, biophysicists experimenting on plants and animals find biological batteries. Sometimes they study large collections of such cells—as in the brain, or in heart muscle—and sometimes they work with single cells, but whatever the biological preparation may be, a measurable electrical phenomenon turns up as it goes about its process of living. The efforts of generations of researchers show that the growing tip of an onion root and the secreting glands of a human stomach follow the same general rules. A single plant cell displays electrical properties remarkably similar to those of a single nerve or muscle cell of the frog. This chapter and the next take up some of the generalizations applying to normally acting nerve and muscle cells—generalizations stemming in large part from measurement of electrical events.

To begin at the beginning, consider the plight of the physiologist setting out to study electrical activity of tissues. He is like someone abandoned on a desert island with an unlabeled phonograph record and no record player. Those grooves on the record hold something fascinating to hear, maybe even beautiful, if only their message could be made intelligible. What does he need to make this message ring out loud and clear? First of all, a needle and pickup cartridge, similar to the physiologist's probing electrode. When the needle moves over the record, the phonograph cartridge will produce about 4 millivolts at frequencies from 20–20,000 cycles per second. When this voltage is amplified and used to activate a loudspeaker, then the message pressed onto the shellac surface is revealed.

The physiologist's electrodes in brain or muscle similarly detect a few millivolts over just about the same frequency range. These small biological electrical changes must also be amplified and converted into forms of energy we can perceive. Half a century of progress in electrode, amplifier, and recording technology has brought the physiologist a long way down the road from blurred and scratchy amplifications of nervous activity toward truly high fidelity recordings. Here, as in the field of sound recording, the problem of faithfully capturing all the details of the message to be studied has not yet been solved entirely.

Measuring Apparatus

Electrodes can be made of any substance that conducts electricity. The metal plates pasted in the EKG lab to the patient's arm and leg are made of zinc, stainless steel, or some other metal not likely to corrode. If the electrode is to penetrate the skin to get at muscle or nerve, a large plate will not do, and here small ones or even bare wires are employed. Some metals—copper and silver, for instance—kill living cells, and biologists generally avoid these in favor of platinum, tungsten, or stainless steel, which do not.

Metals, of course, are not the only substances that conduct electricity. Any paste or fluid containing ions will conduct, and electrodes consisting of glass tubes filled with salt solutions, or merely wicks of cotton soaked in the solution and wrapped around a wire, can be put onto nerve or muscle tissue and readily conduct away the biological currents they generate.

Electrode size makes little difference to its properties except, of course, that the smaller its cross-sectional area the more resistance it offers to the flow of current. Size makes a great deal of difference, however, to the physiologist who wishes to discover what electrical gyrations a single nerve or muscle cell goes through during its activity. A single human red blood corpuscle measures 7 microns across (.0007 cm), human nerve fibers between one and 20 microns, and the largest spinal cord nerve cells perhaps only 150 microns in diameter. With great patience one might tease such a large nerve cell out of the spinal cord and just barely see it with the naked eye. Physiologists don't want to look at it with the eye, however; they want to find out how it behaves electrically when normally in place.

To do this, they have developed microelectrodes—stainless steel or tungsten wire sharpened to an extremely fine tip, or fluid-filled glass pipettes with an opening of 1 micron or less at the sharp end. They push these microelectrodes right down next to a nerve cell, or actually poke through its wall and come to rest inside it, and thus record the electrical events of that cell alone. Much precise information on how nerve and muscles act has come from experiments where microelectrodes were manipulated into position in this way.

Recording devices in physiology have a developmental history that closely parallels, as you might imagine, the growth of new tools devised by physicists for use in their own measurements. One of the first such instruments capable of following the individual discharges of a neuron was the capillary electrometer with which Lucas and Adrian at Cambridge University, in England, observed the rate of discharge of sensory nerves. It consists of a column of mercury in a glass tube with a layer of dilute acid over the mercury. When voltage varies across the mercury-acid interface, the curvature of the mercury surface alters and the height of the mercury column changes slightly. A beam of light thrown across the interface onto a moving strip of photographic film registers the fluctuation.

The string galvanometer developed by Einthoven in 1902 is another early instrument, more sensitive, and still used to record the EKG. In it a fine quartz fiber stretches tightly between the poles of a strong magnet. The fiber is plated with gold. Current coming from the biological tissue flows along the fiber and compels it to move in the magnetic field. A beam of light interrupted by the fiber registers these movements, the amplitude of which is proportional to the current flow.

The most common modern instrument for recording biopotentials appeared in the early 1920s when Gasser,

Erlanger, and Bishop introduced the cathode-ray oscilloscope tube to biology. Unlike the electrometer and galvanometer, in which the tiny biocurrent must move a component with a relatively large mass, the cathode-ray tube utilizes a beam of electrons with negligible mass to write on a fluorescent screen.

The picture tube in a TV set is also a cathode-ray tube; both it and the biologist's instrument operate because the designers applied several simple physical principles in a most ingenious way. In the cathode-ray tube a wire is fixed in place at the socket end of what looks like an oddly-shaped light bulb. This wire, when heated, gives off a cloud of electrons which, being negatively charged, can be made to move toward a positively charged region. A nearby plate of metal bearing a strong positive charge does this job. It has a hole in its center through which many of the electrons escape to speed as a beam toward the front of the tube.

Along the way this stream of electrons must pass between two parallel plates of metal to which charges of electricity can be applied from the outside. If one of these plates is positively charged and the other negatively, the electron beam will be deflected toward the positively charged one. If now we slowly remove the charges from the plates, the electron beam will slowly return to its formerly straight course from one end of the tube to the other. When we connect a nerve or muscle to these plates, movements of the electron beam will instantly and accurately portray any voltage change that occurs in the biological tissue.

But we cannot see an electron beam, and to make its

movements visible the engineers coat the front of the cathode-ray tube with a substance which gives off light when bombarded with electrons. (This material is what gives a TV tube the yellowish-white appearance you see when the set is turned off.) Now if the biological battery changes its voltage we will see a spot of light move up and down on the face of the cathode-ray tube.

In addition to these plates that move the electron beam up and down, cathode-ray tubes have a similar pair of plates that move the beam from side to side. The charge applied to these is generated by an electronic circuit built into the instrument.

At time zero this circuit charges the left-hand plate positive with respect to the other; the electron beam instantly jumps to the left of the screen. As time goes on the charge gradually diminishes to zero—which moves the spot to the center of the screen—and then becomes increasingly negative—which carries it toward the right. This is done so exactly that precisely the same amount of time passes for every inch the spot moves across.

A cathode-ray tube working in a biological experiment thus measures time on its horizontal axis and the biological voltage on its vertical axis. The spot moving across draws the picture the biologist wants to see—how the biological battery changes its voltage as time progresses.*

Amplifiers for raising the smallest bioelectrical voltages to the point where they will drive a recording device

* See Donald G. Fink and David M. Lutyens, *The Physics of Television*, Science Study Series, Doubleday, 1960.

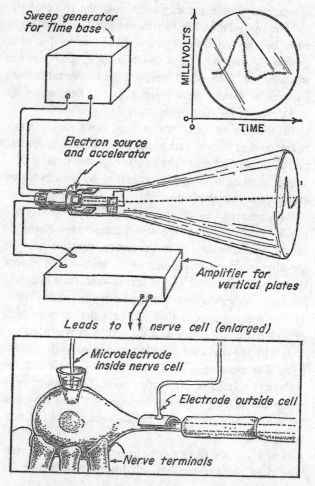

Fig. 9. The modern method of detecting and displaying activity in a single nerve fiber. Cathode ray tube (upper right) displays time course of electrical events.

were first developed about 40 years ago by Gasser, by Forbes at Harvard University, and by many others who made use of the then new vacuum tubes. Nowadays engineers actively work with transistor circuits for this biological application, and a powerful all-transistor amplifier capable of higher fidelity than any amplifier available ten years ago has recently been constructed. It is the size of a book of matches; its counterpart used to be as large as a kitchen stove.

The way a microelectrode, amplifier, and oscilloscope are put together to record the electrical activity of a single cell can be visualized from Fig. 9. The cell shown might have come from the spinal cord (dissected out for purposes of illustration); a microelectrode has been pushed inside it, and the circuit completed through the amplifier and recorder. The trace on the oscilloscope can be photographed to make a permanent record.

A wise man has said, "The smaller the object to be studied the larger the equipment needed for its study." To determine the earth's gravitational field we need only a simple pendulum, while to study the atomic nucleus requires a huge accelerator costing millions. For brain cells and the muscles they activate one needs an assemblage of equipment just about halfway between these extremes in size—and in cost.

The Membrane Theory in Detail

Electrical potential can be produced in a number of ways. An electromotive force can be generated as a result of chemical reaction, as in a battery; by the movement of a conductor in a magnetic field, as in a generator; by the application of heat to a junction of dissimilar metals, as in a thermocouple; by pressure on certain crystalline materials (piezoelectricity), as in a quartz phonograph cartridge; by means of light striking metals and their oxides, as in the photoelectric light meter; by means of separation of charges produced by friction of dissimilar nonconductors (static electricity). The net effect is the same, a movement of electrons through the medium to which the electromotive force is applied.

Since its discovery in the late 18th century, biologists have wondered whether Galvani's "animal electricity" was somehow unique or whether it too could be explained by well-known physicochemical processes. At the present time most biologists feel that bioelectricity can indeed be explained by physical processes, but that the method the cell uses is not exactly any one of those just listed, nor has man ever duplicated the complete process in the laboratory or in industry. Bioelectric potentials appear to be due to the physical separation of positively and negatively charged ions. To understand how this happens in living cells will be easier if we first consider some simple but related nonbiological experiments that illustrate the ideas biologists work with, and will lead to a discussion of their results.

Imagine a thin sheet of cellophane or polyethylene that has submicroscopic holes in it through which small ions will pass but large ones will not. Take a piece, about 10 inches square, fashion a bag from it by folding up the edges, and fill the bag with cold water. Tie a piece of string around the top so that water cannot leak in or out. Now fill a custard dish with water to which a teaspoon of salt and a drop of food dye have been added. Mix well and put the bag of clear water into the dish of colored salty water overnight. In the morning take the bag out, rinse it in tap water, and spill its contents into a clean glass. It will be colored, and it will taste salty, demonstrating that the sheet freely passes the sodium ions and chloride ions which make up salt, as well as the colored molecules of the food dye.

To prove that such a bag will not pass large ions, imagine this experiment. Next time someone breaks an egg in the kitchen, borrow about a teaspoon of it—the white alone, or a mixture of white and yolk will do equally well—and dissolve it in a cupful of cold tap water. Fill one of the little bags with the egg solution, tie it up as before, and again immerse it overnight in water to which salt and dye have been added. In the morning you will find no egg outside the bag, although the dye and salt will again have moved to the inside. An egg is largely composed of protein and fat, and these molecules, when ionized, are too large to pass through the holes in the bag.

One final question. Water molecules are small in size and highly mobile. Hence, they move freely back and forth through the bag wall. If you fill the inside of the bag with large molecules that will not pass through, will there be less or more water inside the bag the morning after?

Now consider the situation where we put into the bag

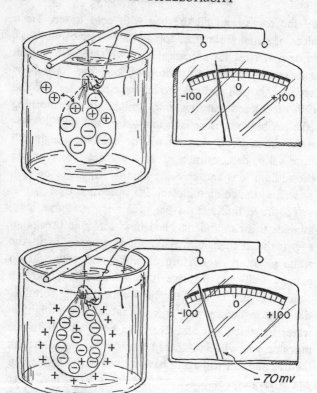

Fig. 10. Experiment to illustrate how unequal distribution of ions could produce voltage difference across a membrane. TOP: *Bag of water containing charged particles immersed in beaker of pure water; voltmeter shows voltage difference between inside of bag and outside.* BOTTOM: *Hours later, at equilibrium, voltmeter shows a stable reading.*

a solution containing a small, positively charged ion and a large, negatively charged ion (Fig. 10). Both ion populations will be in constant, random motion, which is directly proportional to their size and the temperature of the solution. Some of the ions will strike the sides of the bag and pass through the pores. Since the negatively charged ions are too large to squeeze through, an uneven distribution of positive and negative charges—in other words a voltage difference—will exist between the inside and outside of the bag. Yet the electrostatic attraction between the negatively charged particles inside and the positive ones outside will keep them both lined up on the two sides of the membrane.

Thus we see that the potential between the inside and the outside (Fig. 10) would be a result of two fundamental properties of ions in solution—first their tendency to equalize their concentration everywhere (and so the plus ions move through the holes), and, second, the tendency for electrical neutrality to exist between different parts of a solution. Interposition of a membrane through which ion species pass at different rates makes these tendencies oppose each other and thus generate a voltage across the membrane. As the two processes go on, it becomes increasingly difficult for a positively charged ion to tear itself away from the negatively charged interior; it cannot move across the potential gradient in order to take up a place in the positively charged exterior. A point finally is reached where all opposed tendencies exactly balance each other.

The value of the voltage developed at this point can be exactly calculated from an equation developed by the German physicist Nernst. The voltage is proportional to the logarithm of the following ratio: the concentration of the diffusable ion inside the membrane divided by concentration of the ion outside the membrane. Its exact value comes after multiplying this number by a constant which accounts for the temperature of the solutions and the charge on the ions, thus:

$$\text{Voltage} = k \times \log \frac{\text{Conc. ion inside}}{\text{Conc. ion outside}}$$

The Resting Cell

Now it happens that in living cells some chemicals are much more concentrated inside the membrane than they are outside. Potassium ions (K^+), for instance, stand in a ratio of about 20 to 1 when inside cell juice is compared to outside fluid. It has therefore occurred to several people to apply the Nernst equation to living cells and to test whether the 70 millivolt difference in potential across such a cell membrane might be due to nothing but this (K^+) concentration ratio. The test is simple enough. You arrange microelectrode, amplifier, and oscilloscope as shown in Fig. 9 and bathe the nerve cell in fluid containing first one, then another amount of (K^+). When at 20°C the potassium outside the cell is successively varied between normal and 60 times normal, the Nernst equation very neatly reduces to

$$\text{millivolts} = 58 \times \log \frac{(K^+) \text{ inside}}{(K^+) \text{ outside}}$$

Deviations from the theoretical curve appear and cause the experts much trouble, but, to a first approximation, in the nerve and muscle cell at rest this (K^+) ratio goes a long way toward explaining that 70 mv potential which cells display at rest.

Of course, the actual situation turns out to be more complex than this; it always does. The cell membrane is not merely a sieve, and potassium is not the only ion involved. Several experiments show that the membrane pumps certain ions actively into the cell while rejecting others. Because of these and other facts, biologists still cannot be sure they know exactly the distribution of ions on the two sides of a living cell membrane.

This membrane the biologists talk about, though one of their fundamental tenets, has never been clearly seen or photographed even with microscopes of highest power. About all one can say is that *something* (let's call it a membrane) about 50–100 angstrom units thick surrounds the cytoplasm of a nerve or muscle cell. You can poke a hole in it, or tear it, whereupon the cytoplasm from inside the cell spills into the surrounding fluid. But when intact it prevents certain substances from entering the cell and encourages others to do so.

Experiments show it behaves as does a thin layer of oil, and it may actually be composed of a lattice of lipoid and protein molecules. This membrane—whatever it is—also offers resistance to the passage of electrical currents, and its resistance varies over a wide range, depending on whether the cell is active or not. The whole cell, with its membrane, can store an applied electrical charge—which cytoplasm alone cannot do. Many similar observations demand that we postulate this "membrane," but these perhaps are enough for the moment.

Above all, this membrane, this cell boundary, shows selective permeability to potassium and sodium ions, a remarkable physical property which explains for most biologists why nerves can conduct and muscles contract. The 20 to 1 (K^+) ratio we discussed expresses a most unusual selective action toward the potassium ion, resulting in the heavy concentration inside the cell as compared to outside. But with sodium ions (Na^+), the membrane does the reverse. Measurements show about ten times as much (Na^+) *outside* the cell as inside, which means the membrane manages simultaneously to do two different things—concentrate (K^+) *inside* the cell and (Na^+) *outside*. The voltage across the membrane from these two concentration ratios, by the way, does not exactly equal that 70 mv we measure across it because many more ions are distributed unequally between inside and outside. Each ion discrepancy adds or subtracts a little, with 70 mv as the resultant of them all. For our present purposes, however, let us merely consider the two ions (K^+) and (Na^+)—a reasonable position to take, since these two probably account for most of the transmembrane potential we measure.

The situation, then, is like that shown in Fig. 11, in which negative charges (chloride ions and large immobile anions) distribute themselves as best they can to achieve an electrically neutral state on the two sides of the membrane. The 70 mv potential difference across the membrane, with the inside of the cell negative, expresses exactly the degree to which the ions involved are

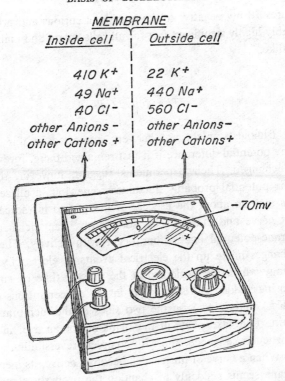

Fig. 11. Ionic concentrations on either side of the cell membrane.

incapable of achieving electrical neutrality. The complex system of ions involved simply cannot manage to overcome, so to speak, the special properties of the membrane in order to redistribute themselves so that the same number of both ions and electrical charges appears inside and outside the cell. In the resting cell the discrepancy is such that the inside almost always measures 70 mv negative to the outside, a curious and probably highly significant fact for all cells—plant and animal alike.

The Active Cell

Biologists might not be very interested in this 70 mv potential difference if it just remained there, forever unchanged. Their experiments suggest, however, that the potential probably fluctuates somewhat in all cells as they go about the process of living, and in the case of nerve and muscle cells, some truly dramatic membrane-potential fluctuations occur with activity. These changes make up the electrical events of electrophysiology which are explained at the present time by supposing sudden shifts to occur in the concentrations of (K^+) and (Na^+) on the two sides of the membrane, shifts that take place in the twinkling of an eye, in a particular sequence, and with complete reversibility.

When a nerve or muscle cell becomes active, its membrane seems suddenly to abandon the property of preventing (Na^+) from entering the cell, whereupon (Na^+) pours inside, destroying its customary concentration gradient and abolishing the resting potential this ion gradient maintains between inside and outside. In an exactly similar manner the membrane of an activated nerve or muscle cell suddenly fails to hold the 20 to 1 (K^+) ratio, whereupon (K^+) pours outward, and again we see dramatic electrical events due to collapse of the potential predicted by the Nernst equation for the resting state. These membrane-permeability changes represent for most modern physiologists the fundamental events that explain nerve and muscle action.

In their timing and sequence these events follow an immutable order. First comes the flow of sodium ions from outside in; this rises to a peak, stops, and reverses —so that (Na^+) is now pumped *out* of the cell—all within .0005 sec. At about the instant (Na^+) movement into the cell reaches its peak, (K^+) ions begin to pour in the opposite direction—out of the cell—but this movement, too, promptly slows and reverses itself, also within about .0005 sec. Thus the membrane permeability rises, first for (Na^+), then for (K^+), and restores itself once more all within a span of a thousandth of a second (1 msec) or so.

Obviously and inevitably, dramatic electrical events accompany the shifting of ions just described. A large potential due to sodium ions stands across the membrane, according to the Nernst rule; its collapse could not only abolish the existing resting potential (70 mv) but actually drive it in the opposite direction. It is so large, in fact, that if sodium ions alone were to move, the 70 mv displayed by the resting cell—inside *negative* —could decrease to zero and grow to perhaps 70 mv— inside *positive*. As we know, however, ions other than sodium move through the membrane of the active nerve and muscle cell—potassium, for instance. And moving potassium ions produce electrical effects also. Since potassium moves outward, furthermore, its electrical effect opposes that of the sodium moving inward. At the moment these two effects exactly balance one another, the

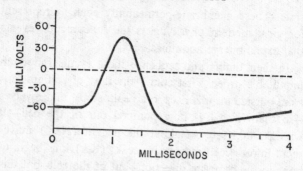

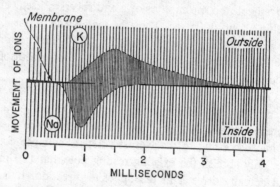

Fig. 12. TOP: *Electrical event recorded at a given spot on a nerve fiber as an impulse sweeps past.* BOTTOM: *Ion movements along a segment of nerve membrane through which an impulse is passing.*

inside of the cell has indeed become positive to the outside, but only by perhaps 20 mv. This equilibrium point represents the peak electrical response achieved in nerve or muscle cell activity. It lasts for only an instant. As we have seen, the membrane promptly restores ionic balance once more, returning the cell to its resting state

—inside cytoplasm registering 70 mv negative to outside fluid, ready to become active all over again. These changes are shown in the accompanying chart (Fig. 12).

Conduction of Impulses

We can expect that the chemical and electrical events just described as occurring at a given spot on the membrane would not be restricted to that location only. After all, the polarized membrane entirely surrounds the cell without breaks or discontinuities, and what happens at one point, especially if it be as spectacular as this membrane failure under discussion, ought to make a difference elsewhere on the cell surface as well. Particularly should this be true, one might guess, at membrane locations just next door to where ions suddenly pour unchecked through what hitherto had been an impenetrable barrier.

It is axiomatic that whenever ions move, electrical currents flow; and, conversely, when currents are flowing, ions are compelled thereby to move. These complementary statements hold, of course, for the movements of the Na and K ions we have been considering. When these ions move, their movement will set current flowing through portions of nearby normal membrane. The membrane immediately adjacent will receive the densest current flow, which means that the Na and K ions standing there—at rest, so to speak—are compelled most strongly to move. This forced movement somehow sets into motion the immutable sequence we already have discussed—inward flow of sodium, outward movement of potassium, and restoration once more of the relationships seen at rest. Meanwhile, however, the normal membrane immediately adjacent to this newly-disturbed region reacts in its turn, and so the membrane events under discussion, wherever started, spread like a prairie fire over the entire cell membrane. Once we excite the cell—force a sufficient number of ions to move at one point—the electrical currents thereby set into motion ensure orderly propagation of that excitation to the most remote reaches of the cell.

The source of electrical energy that drives such an impulse along a nerve fiber is the electrical pressure exerted by different concentrations of sodium and potassium ions outside and inside its membrane. With rise in permeability toward these ions at one point on the membrane, the energy inherent in that electrochemical pressure becomes available; ions penetrate the membrane, electric currents flow, and the nerve impulse spreads along the fiber. When we pinch the ankle of a giraffe, the ion movements roused spread via leg and spinal cord all the way to the brain some 30 feet away.

Conduction of the impulse along nerves occurs at rates varying between about 1 meter and 100 meters per sec, as we already have seen. In the nerves of primitive animals, and in the very smallest fibers of all forms, the rates measured are slow. The highest rates occur in nerve fibers ensheathed by a fatty substance, myelin, which is continuous except for tiny breaks—nodes of Ranvier—that occur every few millimeters. Myelin conducts electric currents very poorly, and so local electric current cannot act in passing the disturbance to *immediately* adjacent regions of membrane. What happens instead is that current passes out of one of the tiny breaks in the myelin where ions are moving and in at the next tiny break some millimeters away, where it sets K and Na ions into motion in the usual manner. Conduction proceeds, in other words, not smoothly but by leaps and bounds, with large intervening regions of the membrane left entirely untouched by the process. As might be expected, this saltatory (Latin *saltare,* to jump or dance) conduction characterizes those neurons which must pass their message most quickly from here to there.

But however slowly or speedily the nerve may act, its message is essentially the news that a short time ago Na ions poured in through the membrane some distance away. A pin stuck into the finger starts Na ions to move there and the news that this has happened passes inward to the brain. In motor nerves—the ones passing to muscles—the Na movement originates within the brain, progresses outward to the muscle, and upon arrival there eventually produces muscle contraction by first compelling Na ions to move in the membrane of the muscle itself. The "message" of a nerve, then, amounts to nothing more than the information that a chemical event of a membrane (the Na and K story) got under way not long ago back up the line.

CHAPTER 5

ACTIVATING CELLS IN THE BODY

How nerve messages normally get started in the body—
the problem of nerve excitation—has occupied many
physiologists for many years. Galvani discovered a way
to excite them artificially, as we have seen, by passing
electrical currents through them, and the mechanism in
such cases should by now be clear. However, Galvani's
way of forcing ions to move (by driving battery currents
through the nerve) is obviously not exactly the way
nerves naturally become roused into action. What do
we know about their natural activation within the normal body?

Activation at Sense Organs

Let us look first at sensory nerves, the ones naturally
excited by pinpricks, sounds, lights, taste-substances,
and so on. What happens in the nerves of the ear, eye,
or tongue at the instant the nerve impulse begins?

Consider the nerves enabling us to smell. Each starts
out as a naked cluster of little terminals high up in the

back of the nose, and these collect together into a nerve fiber that passes up into the brain. The naked little nerve endings in the nose are exposed to air currents that sweep over them with every breath. If the air is what we call "pure," its gas molecules fail to arouse activity in the endings. But if the air stream brings, say, perfume molecules into the nose, these chemical substances touch the nerve terminals, agitate the Na ions there, and thus set off the membrane events with which we are by now familiar. In this instance some particular chemical substance, a perfume molecule, arouses the nerve into action, and this idea—that certain chemicals readily excite nerves while others do not—is fundamental. For as in the nose, so throughout the nervous system wherever nerve terminals lie freely exposed—specific chemical substances can and often do arouse them to action.

But in addition to applying chemical substances directly to naked nerve endings as in the nose, the body in other places employs a method rather like Galvani's battery. The case of the ear clearly illustrates this; here specialized cells act much as does the pickup cartridge of a phonograph to convert mechanical motion induced by the sound waves into biological electrical potentials that in turn excite the nerve endings.

The accompanying figure shows the biological structures involved and the essential events in the ear, where sound waves become converted into nerve impulses. Movement of the ear drum by sound waves causes motion of the bones attached to it, whereupon the delicate inner membrane on which the other end of the bone sits moves also, as does the liquid which that delicate mem-

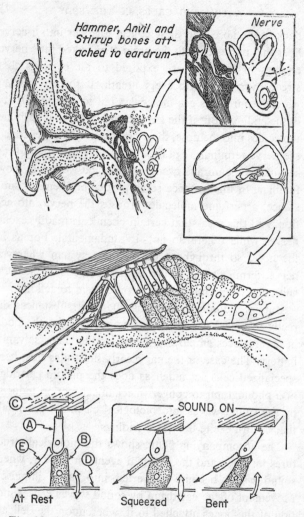

Hammer, Anvil and
Stirrup bones att-
ached to eardrum

Nerve

SOUND ON

C
A
E
B
D

At Rest   Squeezed   Bent

Fig. 13. The human ear with diagrams, based on electron microscope pictures, of the innermost parts at work.

brane keeps dammed up inside the head. The fluid-filled innermost portion of the ear is called the cochlea, and it is here that the motions created by sound waves are converted into the nerve impulses that make hearing possible. The insert of Fig. 13 shows just where this series of events comes to fruition. Cell (A) is called a hair cell because one of its borders contains fine filaments embedded in and held fast by an overlying structure, (C), the tectorial membrane. Cell (A) is supported by cell (B), which in turn rests firmly upon a thin membrane, (D), suspended within the fluids of the inner ear. This membrane (D) and the tectorial membrane (C) can readily move with respect to one another, (C) remaining relatively rigid when a sound agitates the inner-ear fluids while (D) moves up and down freely in the direction of the arrows. The end result of this differential motion of (C) and (D) is that the movement squeezes, twists, and otherwise displaces cells (A) and (B) relative to the hairs imprisoned by the stable structure (C). An immediate consequence of this motion is generation of an electrical potential—probably by cell (A)—proportional to the magnitude of the movement, and this potential produces the event we are here interested in—arousal of an impulse in the nerve fiber, (E). Once the nerve becomes activated its impulse, of course, proceeds toward the brain (in the direction shown). The hearing mechanism at this level turns out, therefore, to be an ingenious device for converting sound waves into flowing electrical currents for the purpose of rousing nerve fibers to action.

Several other sense organs in the body evidently use

this same principle in order to convert variations of mechanical pressure into nerve impulses. The balance organ near the cochlea is one of them. It provides information about the head's position with respect to gravity, and so helps make it possible to know in the dark whether our eyes—if we could see in the dark—would be directed toward the horizon, up into the sky, or where. A system of hair cells remarkably like those of the cochlea seems here also to generate electrical currents that activate nerve fibers to make this possible.

Another structure, the Pacinian corpuscle inside the abdomen, gives information about pressure and distention (being activated vigorously, for instance, as a big Christmas dinner goes on and on). You might easily mistake a Pacinian corpuscle under the microscope for an onion, with its many thin layers of tissue each completely surrounding the next-smaller layer inside. At the very center of the "onion" is embedded a nerve fiber ending; it promptly responds whenever the outermost layers of the Pacinian corpuscle are mechanically displaced, squeezed, or twisted; the distortion starts electrical currents flowing.

From the preceding discussion we have seen the body use in one place chemical and in another electrical methods to get nerve impulses under way. These two methods are clearly the ones most commonly used to get nerves into action. But in several cases—the eye for one—physiologists are hard put to tell whether the chemical or the electrical method predominates, since both appear to be employed. This illustrates a difficulty that has always plagued the physical scientist attempting to analyze nerve activity: often several physical principles obviously are being applied simultaneously, and he cannot readily extricate one of them to study it apart from the other.

Both chemical and electrical events can be seen at work in the brain itself, to which we are about to turn. More than fifty years of intense discussion and thousands of experiments attempting to discover their relative importance have not yet brought us the final answers.

Activating Nerve Cells within the Brain

Most discussions of brain function emphasize the paramount importance of the synapses, the name given to those places within the nervous system where one nerve ends and another begins. The two neurons involved at a synapse never touch directly, a space measuring about 200 angstroms always separating them. In fact, a space of the same dimension separates each nerve cell from any other cell it abuts against, as, for example, cells (A) and (B) in the figure of the cochlea.

An angstrom unit of length is very small indeed—10^{-8} ($\frac{1}{100,000,000}$) cm—and biological measurements expressed in such small units can be made only with the most modern type of microscope, the electron microscope. This instrument, developed by physicists and used by biologists, illustrates once again the close interplay of the two groups of scientists who freely exchange their tools and ideas for mutual benefit. Before getting down to the synapse in detail, let us make a side excursion into electron microscopy of the brain. This will give us a glimpse at its most intimate structure.

First of all, however, what physical principles are put to work in the operation of an electron microscope? Several of the same ones we saw employed in the cathode-ray tube, and some new ones. An electron microscope is basically a hollow metal tube some inches or feet in length with a heated-wire electron source at one end and a positive target at the other. Several hundred thousand volts drive the electrons straight down the tube from their source to the target. To guide and control their path the stream of electrons is deflected—as in a cathode-ray tube—by a nearby magnetic or electrostatic field. Creating such fields at the right place permits focusing the electron microscope beam to a tiny spot at exactly the point where the object to be magnified is located, and then spreading the beam over a large area after it has passed beyond. The magnification achieved is given by the ratio of the cross section of the beam at its smallest and largest dimensions. Magnifications of 10,-000 or more are common for modern instruments.

Placing a photographic film in the path of the electron beam where its diameter is largest allows the microscopist to make a permanent record of the object of his study. When electrons strike a photographic emulsion, they act upon it exactly as light does, producing a latent image later developed in the usual way. This photograph, showing where electrons did not strike the film and where they did, reflects accurately the corresponding regions in the magnified article where electrons were absorbed and where they were not.

The object to be magnified, placed at the point where the electron beam is most concentrated, must be sliced into a very thin sheet. Otherwise, no electrons at all would pass through it. Brain tissue studied in this way must first be hardened with chemicals, then embedded in plastic from which slices, a fraction of a micron thick, are shaved. One such slice, placed carefully on a tiny metal screen, is passed through a door in the side of the electron microscope tube and clamped in place at the focus of the electron beam. The door is then closed and the air removed from the tube with a vacuum pump, since collisions between electrons and air molecules inside the tube would distort and spoil the photograph. Once the tube is free of air, the operator starts the electrons flowing, adjusts the magnetic fields, positions the brain section so that it shows what he wishes, and takes the picture.

Fig. 14 shows in semidiagrammatic form how an electron microscope picture of a synaptic region within the brain might look. The nerve cell receiving impulses fills the lower half of the picture; part of its nucleus is showing. Impulses sweep toward the cell in the direction of the arrows along the nerve endings of a nerve fiber that might have been activated—as in the case of the giraffe —several meters away. Where incoming neurons meet the receiving neuron, we see an empty, narrow space whose borders consist of dense and darkened areas. This is the region of the synapse, the place where the nerve message passes from one cell to the next. These dark-

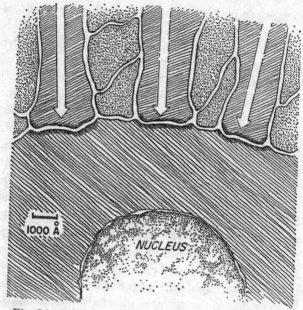

1000 Å

NUCLEUS

Fig. 14. At billions of contacts between nerves like the three shown here, incoming messages (moving in direction of the arrows) activate receiving neurons in brain and spinal cord.

ened areas of nerve membrane regularly appearing at synapses probably represent a dense concentration of chemical substances necessary for passing the impulse across the empty synaptic space.

The most popular current theory of synaptic action supposes the naked portion of the receiving neuron (in the lower half of the picture) to act much as does the smell nerve in the nose; incoming nerve impulses squirt tiny jets of some chemical into the synaptic space and thus influence the membrane of the receiving neuron. The chemical involved here is not, of course, the perfume molecule as in the nose. Its identity has not yet been firmly established, but it could be the powerful, naturally occurring drug, acetylcholine.

The essential point of this modern theory is worth repeating: synapses work because an impulse arriving at the junction between two neurons releases a chemical substance that crosses over the gap and activates the naked neuron on the opposite side, a series of events occurring within only 1 msec or so. Some years ago the process of nerve-impulse transmission at synapses was thought to involve mainly electrical events, but these now are regarded as less important than the chemical ones.

Perhaps you have been wondering about the stippled cells shown in Fig. 14. These are glia cells, not nerve cells, and the brain contains immense numbers of them. The electron microscope shows them to be everywhere in the most intimate possible contact with neurons and with one another, as the figure shows. The regions where glia cells make contact with one another and with neurons have been called gliapses, to contrast them with the synapses, which are purely neuro-neural contacts. What gliapses have to do with brain function is an open question, and as yet almost no research has been done on the problem.

Nerve-Muscle Synapses

In order to clarify the chemical events that occur at nerve-nerve synapses, it will be helpful to consider what transpires at nerve-muscle synapses. Nerves do make synaptic contacts with muscle fibers, and muscles contract or shorten because a stream of impulses descends upon them through these synapses. The chemical events operating at these nerve-muscle junctions are by now fairly well understood, and we may safely assume that much the same sequence of events must operate—in principle at least—at the nerve synapses within the brain.

At this point you might re-examine with profit the diagram on page 48 showing the way motor nerves emerge from the spinal cord and pass out to the muscles they innervate. A muscle fiber ordinarily receives only one nerve fiber, the junction between them being called an end-plate. The details of this end-plate region can be seen in Fig. 15, a drawing taken from an electron microscope photograph. The nerve cell here, as everywhere, is separated from its neighbors by a space measuring about 200 angstrom units. Glia cells surround the nerve here as in the brain, but at the junction between nerve and muscle nothing whatever intervenes. Notice that a dense layer of material characterizes the nerve ending at this location just as it does at synaptic regions in the brain itself. Evidently the nerve-muscle junction closely resembles a nerve-nerve junction in several important respects, not the least important of which is that

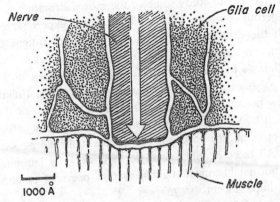

Fig. 15. The junction of a nerve with its muscle resembles the contacts between nerves shown in Fig. 14.

both display the dense layer of chemical substance that is vital for passing the message from one cell to the next.

Now if we could know what chemical events occur at this junction between a motor nerve and its muscle—where the nerve message calls forth muscle contraction—we could reasonably argue that exactly similar ones probably occur at brain synapses also. The membrane of a resting muscle fiber is, after all, exactly like that of a resting nerve, capable of being depolarized, whereupon Na and K ions pour back and forth in the well-known orderly way. Can it be shown that the ion movements that convert the resting muscle fiber into a contracting one originate when the nerve fiber squirts a tiny amount of a particular chemical substance into the space between the two? If so, what is the chemical?

Obtaining today's answer to these questions has led

physiologists to study some of the most fascinating and dangerous poisons known. They have experimented with the drug cocaine; extract of the ergot fungus of grain, consumption of which produced epidemics of "St. Anthony's fire" in the Middle Ages; derivatives of all the poisonous mushrooms; the South American Indian arrow poison, curare; strychnine, from the seeds of the Indian tree *Strychnos nux-vomica;* and the most lethal poison of all, the botulinus bacillus toxin of food poisoning. All these deadly agents do their work by jamming the normal chemical machinery that operates to conduct impulses across synapses.

We will consider here only the Indian arrow poison, curare, for it has played a key role in unraveling the story of where and how the synaptic chemicals work. Curare acts at the nerve-muscle junction where the nerve ending is known to produce the chemical acetylcholine (ACh in shorthand) that crosses the end-plate region and activates the muscle beyond. There is reason to believe this ACh acts at specific spots upon the muscle membrane, spots too small to be identifiable even under electron microscope magnification. These tiny regions, called receptive sites, have a particular chemical affinity for the ACh molecule, absorbing it the way a hungry dog wolfs down beefsteak. ACh absorption promptly yields muscle membrane depolarization and muscle contraction.

But muscle receptive sites will accept a few other molecules besides ACh, of which curare is one, and the combination of receptive sites with curare yields no contraction whatever. Worse yet, when curare is already there, ACh cannot combine with a receptor site. Hence nerve impulses, no matter how abundant the ACh they produce at synapses, cannot arouse a curarized muscle to action.

When the Amazon Indian sharpens his blowgun darts, dips their tips into a bowl of sticky curare, and sets off on a hunting expedition, success comes whenever his aim is good enough to get the tip of the dart under the skin of his prey. He doesn't need to hit a vital spot, for a good dose of curare introduced into the body is picked up by the blood stream, circulated to every nerve-muscle end-plate in the body, and combined with all the receptor sites. The curare prevents the inward movement of Na ions that ACh normally causes in muscle membrane, and thus it completely paralyzes the wounded animal. For these reasons the skillful—and hungry—Amazonian hunter, having merely winged a bird in flight, sees it flutter helplessly to the ground shortly thereafter. As he eats the bird still later, he need not be concerned about the curare its muscles contain, because digestive juices destroy the poison.

The Electric Fish

The curare experiments help to reveal, then, that the nerve-muscle junction operates mainly because a powerful natural chemical—acetylcholine—acts at receptor sites to induce movements of ions in the muscle fiber. But ion movements mean current flow, which is to say, electrical events. And so here we are again, with chemical and electrical events proceeding almost simultaneously to puzzle and challenge any experimenter who would put each in its proper place.

If nature provides through curare a tool for analyzing the chemical aspects of the process, she gives us in the electric fish an outstanding example of emphasis upon the purely electrical aspects. If you put your hand upon a contracting muscle, your biceps for instance, you feel no electric shock when it contracts because the flowing currents generated at the nerve-muscle endings are small and scarcely penetrate the skin. But if you were to put your hand into water near an electric fish, you might receive a stunning shock, because this animal generates large currents, which flow freely through the water in which it swims.

The fish uses its nerve-muscle junctions to produce this shock, thus emphasizing for us the electrical events going on at those junctions. By a kind of evolution-in-reverse, nature has changed some of the fish's muscle fibers into mere membranes that produce not contraction but only membrane-potential change. Layer upon layer, these nerve-muscle junctions lie beneath the skin of the electric eel, stacked vertically like coins. The acetylcholine squirted out by the nerve impulses simultaneously discharges all these nerve-muscle junctions, whereupon the 70 mv electric response of each adds in series to that of the others, and a brief but powerful current flow results. A healthy eel will generate fully 1 ampere of current driven by 600 volts. Except for lightning, such current flows may well have been the first manifestations of electricity observed by man (Fig. 16).

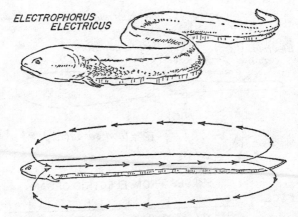

Fig. 16. A South American fish generates an electric shock strong enough to stun a horse. Arrows show direction of current flow in the surrounding water.

But not all electric fish produce stunning and powerful shocks. Some generate throughout life a continuous steady stream of pulses of low voltage. These they use for exploring the watery world they inhabit. Like the bat whose ultrasonic cries probe the space through which he will fly,* these fish apparently use their electrical fields to explore their environment. An object in the water distorts the electric field they create, and this aberration the fish senses through receptors on its body surface (Fig. 17). The fish can easily tell a piece of wire from a stone because one conducts electricity while the other does not.

These animals become agitated by a magnet brought

*See Donald R. Griffin, *Echoes of Bats and Men*, Science Study Series, Doubleday, 1959.

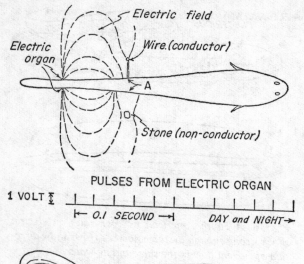

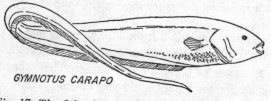

Fig. 17. *The fish whose electric organ serves as a kind of underwater radar. Disturbances in lines of current flow produced by even small wires or stones can be detected.*

close to the aquarium, and they readily detect the electrostatic charge in a comb that has been passed through hair. The measurements show their sensitivity to a change in electric fields to be almost incredibly delicate (0.003 microvolts per mm at threshold). The fundamental questions of what sense organs the fish uses to detect these fields, and how his detection system works, remain largely unsolved.

Subtle Actions at Synapses

Suppose now we go back to the Amazon Indian out hunting birds with his poisoned darts. What would happen if he got a near-miss, merely scraping the bird's skin and thereby introducing a tiny dose of curare into its blood stream to block off only half the receptive sites in its nerve-muscle junctions? The remaining normal receptive sites should still take up ACh and so we can guess that the bird would be half-paralyzed. Would a smaller-than-normal response in such a half-paralyzed muscle tell us some new things about synaptic events?

Fig. 18 shows how an experiment designed to answer this question would be (and actually has been) done on frog tissue. The muscle fiber from the frog nerve-muscle preparation must be impaled with a microelectrode, recordings of the potential between it and the electrode outside being made in the usual way.

The muscle is to be activated by applying an electric shock to the nerve and thus arousing a nerve impulse that sweeps down to the nerve-muscle junction, crosses it, and produces contraction. Tiny drops of the poison curare—very dilute—will be dripped out of a glass tube directly above the nerve-muscle junction. As drop after drop is added, more and more muscle receptor sites will be attacked by the curare until finally no site remains free of the poison.

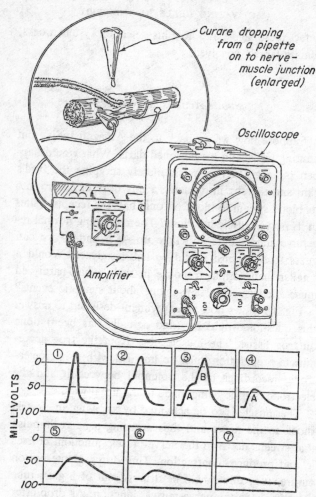

Fig. 18. A single muscle fiber impaled with a microelectrode (TOP) produces changing electrical responses (BOTTOM). The normal potential aroused by
nerve stimulation (1) drops as curare interferes with
nerve-muscle action.

Record (1), taken before the first curare drop, gives the muscle's electrical response as the nerve impulse arrives at the nerve-muscle junction, crosses over, and causes a normal muscle contraction. Record (2) unfolds the first effects of curare which in record (3) stand out clearly. The apparently single electrical response of the normal muscle is breaking down into two parts, (A) and (B). Part (B) disappears completely with addition of still more of the poison [record (4)], and at this instant muscle contraction disappears, too, a clear demonstration that (B), whatever its origin, must be intimately related to the chief business of muscle fibers, which is to contract. Part (A) clearly is something else; a quantity of curare sufficient to paralyze the muscle does not eliminate it and so does not entirely prevent depolarization. Some receptive sites must still be free to combine with ACh, and they generate fully 40 mv of depolarizing potential. Records (5) to (7) reveal that this potential declines still further with additional increments of curare, however, falling steadily toward zero as the poison leaves fewer and fewer receptive sites available to combine with ACh.

This analysis of the electrical response in a progressively poisoned muscle does then suggest additional general principles about synaptic action. The effect of a given-sized nerve impulse upon the postsynaptic element need not be constant. In our example part (A) varied from fully 40 mv in record (4) to almost nothing in record (7), an extraordinary range.

Now if the postsynaptic response can vary its magnitude this much in a poisoned muscle, the question arises whether—at synapses elsewhere—the amount of activity produced by normal presynaptic elements can also vary over a similar range. Perhaps at brain synapses (like those in Fig. 14), a particular incoming element always produces a large effect while some other one always produces a small effect. It could even be obligatory that the two act jointly to cause depolarization in the cell upon which they converge. Such ideas about subthreshold synaptic action—small depolarizing effects incapable by themselves of causing the full postsynaptic response, but obviously leading up to it in some manner—form the basis of modern thinking about synaptic actions in the brain.

The EPSP

A special name is given to these small and subtle depolarizing potentials we must now talk about—excitatory postsynaptic potentials, or EPSPs in the physiologist's shorthand. Intracellular microelectrodes in both nerve and muscle show that the postsynaptic element invariably generates EPSPs during synaptic action. Nerve EPSPs may indeed be large or small in size, as our analysis of the curarized muscle fiber suggested. And even when the postsynaptic cell fails to respond normally, it generally still displays an EPSP, however reduced its size may be.

Our knowledge of these EPSPs in brain cells comes from some of the most elegant experiments ever performed on the nervous systems of cats, frogs, squids, and even insects. Since the nervous systems of several sea-living animals like the lobster lend themselves admirably to EPSP analysis, the experiments often have been done in pleasant laboratories at the seashore in the summer time.

For our example, however, the frog can serve just as well as some exotic animal plucked from the sea. The accompanying figure (Fig. 19) shows a spinal cord nerve cell of a frog upon which three different presynaptic endings [(A), (B), and (C)] converge. An intracellular microelectrode connected in the usual way to an oscilloscope will display any EPSP produced by incoming impulses.

As the accompanying records show, a presynaptic nerve impulse via (A) promptly provokes a large EPSP that quickly dies away. (Note the close and obvious similarity between this response and that of the curarized muscle fiber shown in Fig. 19.) The EPSP provoked via input (B), terminating upon a dendrite of the recipient neuron, turns out to be smaller in size and somewhat more prolonged than that of (A). Neither (A) nor (B) alone causes complete depolarization in the recipient neuron, but when (A) and (B) inputs arrive together they add, and their summed effect sends the recipient nerve cell into action.

This idea that EPSPs summate their effects in the recipient neuron is absolutely fundamental in modern concepts of the operation of brain and spinal cord. To illustrate the idea with a specific example, let us suppose the recipient neuron in our figure goes to a muscle fiber that helps to pull the frog's leg away from a hot object.

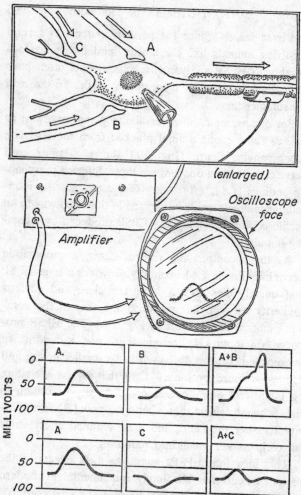

Fig. 19. Nerve cell impaled by microelectrode (TOP) for study of electrical response evoked from it by incoming impulses (BOTTOM). An impulse arriving at position A causes somewhat more activity than one ar-

Let us further suppose that neuron (A) comes from a sense organ in the same leg—a receptor that sends a nerve impulse toward the spinal cord at once when the leg gets hot. Now let's say that the neuron (B) arises within the brain itself; it will show activity only so long as the frog is awake and alert. If the frog were to be chloroformed, neuron (B) would become silent.

Ordinarily then, with the frog alert, a sensory message from the hot foot causes leg withdrawal because (A) and (B) neurons simultaneously provoke their EPSPs. If the frog should be anesthetized, however, the EPSP of (B) would not occur, and the EPSP from (A) alone cannot activate the recipient neuron. The drugged frog fails to respond, then, because there is no summation of the separate EPSPs produced by (A) and (B).

Excitation and Inhibition

Like the frog, I, too, pull my arm away if I accidentally touch a hot radiator with my finger. The reason both his reflex response and mine operate with exact precision can perhaps be visualized from the accompanying figure (Fig. 20) of the so-called reflex arc we both possess. In this reflex arc the first elements, sensory nerves, span the distance from finger to spinal cord; all impulses aroused in the finger traverse them and are dis-

---

riving at B, *but neither depolarizes the receiving nerve completely. A and B arriving together produce a full response. At* C *the arriving impulse provokes an electrical response of opposite sign.*

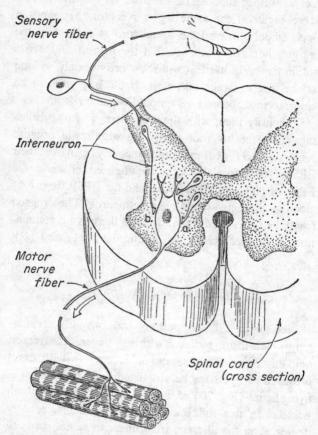

Sensory
nerve fiber

Interneuron

Motor
nerve
fiber

Spinal cord
(cross section)

Fig. 20. Jerking the finger away from a hot object takes
place because nerve impulses pass along circuits like
those shown here.

tributed to very many spinal cord neurons, where they produce EPSPs. The outflowing elements in the reflex arc are the spinal motor neurons depolarized under this barrage of EPSPs. They pass their impulses outward to activate the muscle that jerks the arm away. The completed reflex arc is thus a great circle route in which impulses travel from body surface to spinal cord and brain and then out again to muscles. Here we can see the fundamental path for so much of the neural activity underlying our behavior. You and I, the frog, and even the lowly earthworm, would all be helpless without our reflex arcs.

But not all neurons reside as do the sensory and motor neurons of the reflex arc—partly inside and partly outside the spinal cord. Many nerve cells—indeed, the vast majority—both start and end inside the brain and spinal cord itself. Their messages therefore arise out of prior neuron activity and result in still more neuron activity. As middlemen between incoming and outgoing impulses, these interneurons perform crucially valuable functions in modulating and regulating brain activity.

To get a concrete picture of the dominant role the interneurons play, let us consider once more the painful experience of touching a hot radiator. I need not always jerk my hand away by reflex. I can know the radiator is hot, deliberately put a finger on it—and keep it there despite the discomfort experienced. In other words, my purely reflex response can be prevented, or inhibited, if I wish. Now that we have some idea of what causes a reflex in the first place, we must find a nervous mechanism that enables us to prevent or inhibit the occurrence of reflex.

As we saw in Fig. 19, simply adding EPSPs from several sources determines whether the incoming message will successfully arouse a motor nerve to action. To deal with inhibition, we need some equally simple and logical mechanism for preventing this barrage of EPSPs from achieving the successful depolarization they otherwise would attain. What can be the mechanism of this inhibition at synapses?

How our present-day answer to this question came about illustrates perfectly the power of biophysics, that half-biological, half-physical discipline. The biological half poses the problem in its essence. A man may, if he wishes, burn his hand to a crisp in a flame (as stoical American Indians were said to have done), though ordinarily a protective reflex causes him to withdraw it from far lesser heat. Biology also identifies the place to look for inhibition—at synapses in brain and spinal cord —for events here probably lie at the basis of both the withdrawal and the nonwithdrawal of the hand. And now physics comes into the picture, providing not only amplifiers, oscilloscopes, and similar hardware, but also hard-won concepts like electrical theory, to make the biological measurements possible. The two disciplines, wedded into biophysics, together give the scientist his fighting chance to come up with the answer he seeks.

What, then, do the biophysical measurements show to be the mechanism of inhibition? A relatively simple phenomenon, it turns out: the generation at synapses of *inhibitory* postsynaptic potentials (abbreviation IPSP).

Whenever an inhibitory neuron delivers its impulse at the synapse, it creates in the recipient neuron an event whose electrical sign is opposite to that of an excitatory neuron. IPSPs oppose EPSPs; when an IPSP occurs along with an EPSP, the two cancel out and the recipient neuron shows no response at all. (See Fig. 19.)

We may suppose, then, that an automatic, built-in response, such as withdrawal from a painful stimulus, becomes inhibited when a counterbarrage of IPSPs descends upon the motor neurons and neatly cancels out the EPSPs. Where this counterbarrage of IPSPs originates in the brain, the next and very large question, is one a book like this can scarcely hope to answer fully.

But certainly a few words about how we get ideas and then carry them out belongs here. When we decide to leave the finger on the hot radiator and then actually do it through an effort of the will, the IPSPs we can measure must have originated in depolarizations of neurons one step back from the synapse involved. But where did that nerve depolarization back there originate? Obviously in a still earlier one—and so it will go if we try to trace our decisions and willed acts to their ultimate origin. Our will, our volitions, our ideas begin, so far as biophysics has illuminated these matters, somewhere within the brain as nerve depolarizations which generate in turn still more of the same until finally the muscles cause movement or speech. If there is some place in the "mind" where the process actually begins, it has certainly not been clearly identified.

Many of our decisions and actions, however, depend as much on what transpires outside the body as on what goes on inside the brain. Electromagnetic waves striking the eye prompt us to recognize a friend and say hello to him, and physical vibrations in the air carry his words of greeting back to our ear so that we may know whether his mood is good or bad today. In this case the sensory input controls our responses by starting nerve depolarizations in eye and ear that spread throughout the brain. The marks they make, EPSPs and IPSPs, when mixed with countless others generated by the brain itself, end up finally in the idea, the willed act, or the spoken word.

Keeping the finger on the hot radiator reduces then only in part to the physical chemistry of neurons discussed in this chapter. Understanding behavior and the mind will come, we can suppose, with a more precise description of the interactions among large groups of neurons. Some of the biophysical investigations pointed toward obtaining the information needed to settle this matter form the subject of the next chapter.

CHAPTER 6

ELECTRICAL OUTPUT
OF THE BRAIN

Have you ever wondered what goes on in the brain when you hear a sound? Suppose a firecracker blasts off nearby; you *hear* the noise, you *jump,* and you may become *frightened*.

By now you should have a good general idea of what must transpire in such a situation: that sound jars the eardrum, jiggles the cells in the inner ear, and thus sets off nerve impulses that spread through the brain in some orderly way. Biophysical studies have been a great help in defining where the nerve impulses go, how long they take to get there, and what they do upon arrival.

Fig. 21 shows one major path along which the impulses proceed. From anatomical studies we know that this nervous pathway, the auditory pathway, extends from the cochlea (where nerve excitation begins) forward through the brain to its highest level, the cortex. In several well-defined places along this route nerve cells end and other nerve cells begin. These regions, called brain nuclei, prove to be relay stations for the nerve messages. At the synapse here incoming cells provoke EPSPs and IPSPs from cells that will carry the message

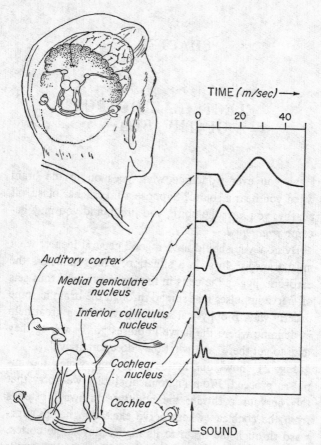

Fig. 21. The brain has been cut away to expose the nerve pathways concerned with hearing. Sounds activate the cochlea first and the auditory cortex last.

forward. When the thousands of synapses collected together in such a nucleus become activated simultaneously, they generate a characteristic electrical event. The figure shows the electrical patterns that would be evoked from the various nuclei of a cat brain by a firecracker explosion.

Study of these electrical responses enables us to trace the progress of the auditory message through the brain. The sudden brief sound produces prompt action in all the nuclei. But the action is not simultaneous everywhere: it appears first at the cochlea, turns up slightly later at the cochlear nucleus in the brain, and then progressively later at stations farther and farther forward. Notice, however, that it takes only 10 msec for the message to arrive at the cortex, the end-station of the auditory pathway. Since cortex is separated from the ear by about 5 cm in the cat, the all-over conduction velocity can be computed to be about 5 meters (15 feet) per second. Obviously the synaptic relays offer little impediment to speedy transmission of the message from the ear to the highest brain level.

The wave shape and duration of responses recorded at the different relay stations provide another interesting fact to contemplate. Near the cochlea the responses come early and are short-lasting; farther along the pathway they not only start later but last longer. This is the general rule: response to a stimulus takes longer to become complete as the nerve message travels farther and farther from its place of origin. No one knows exactly what significance this fact has for the phenomena of hearing. Presumably the brain acts more and more deliberately, and progressively so, mixing, comparing, or in some other way processing the incoming information, but the details of what goes on have not yet been worked out. It would be especially desirable to know what that prolonged activity at the cortical station signifies, for most physiologists suspect that cortex activity must occur if we are to hear and recognize familiar sounds.

So much, then, for how biophysics allows one to make a more sophisticated analysis of what happens when one hears a firecracker go off. How about the startled jump?

This reaction to loud sound, the so-called startle pattern, has been carefully studied with high-speed moving pictures and other techniques. A person startled by such a sound closes his eyes, bends his head so that chin touches chest, brings his elbows next to his body and bends his knees. These movements proceed in a precise order over which the individual has little if any control and seem to be designed to keep him from being hurt. Even when a person knows the loud sound is coming, he cannot entirely prevent the startle pattern from appearing.

As for what goes on in the brain to produce the startle pattern, biophysical studies upon animals have so far revealed, unfortunately, only a part of the total story. The available analysis shows that the incoming message from the ear leaves the auditory pathway and enters other parts of the brain. The nerves carrying the message make synaptic connections there in an area that controls movements of the eyelids, head, arms and legs. As soon as impulses reach this area, a synchronized burst of nerve impulses departs from it, and the individual displays the typical startle pattern of movements. This much we can reasonably deduce from the electrical activity displayed, but the critical brain area where the input message triggers off the stereotyped pattern of muscle movements has yet to be identified.

And now what about the brain events that explain your fright when the firecracker goes off? Intensely personal feelings like fright, hunger, love and hate fall into a class of human responses that have persistently defied scientific analysis. Very little indeed is known about them even by the biophysicists, who, incidentally, have only just recently begun to investigate them. We may suppose, however, that in principle the brain events underlying an emotional response like fright must closely resemble those that produce the startle pattern. To be specific, this is what probably happens: (1) dispersal of impulses away from the main auditory pathways to (2) some distant brain region where (3) EPSPs and IPSPs activate neurons that produce (4) the emotion in question.

A key idea in this scheme is that there should be a brain region whose neurons have the property of producing emotions. Until recently in the realm of speculation, this idea lately has received what many call spectacular experimental support. Studies on rats, cats and monkeys with wires embedded in their brains reveal that these animals will work hard day and night to obtain electrical shocks—provided the wires through which the shocks are delivered lie in certain specific brain regions. When such an animal seeks out electric shocks, himself pushing the switch to turn them on if given the opportunity to do so, it is difficult to avoid the conclusion that he derives some sort of "pleasure" from the experience. And if he does, this means that certain brain regions do indeed produce emotions, as the scheme in the preceding paragraph supposes. We must admit, however, that only future experiments can reveal whether noise from a nearby firecracker produces fright by activating a specific brain region whose function is to produce an emotion.

Though unproven as yet, this conclusion seems attractive and reasonable to most students of brain function. Measurements of brain electrical responses, such as they are, do not rule it out. It is an attractive conclusion, furthermore, for if we accept it, the three behavioral responses we set out to examine—hearing, startle and fear—receive the same fundamental explanation: the nerves aroused to activity in the ear distribute their message to three different brain areas, each of which serves a different special function. One brain area processes the messages to yield the sensation of sound. Another galvanizes body muscles into action. The third produces a series of events—still poorly understood by science—that everyone recognizes as fear. "Now," the experimenters say, "let us find out whether or not the idea is correct."

The human brain contains approximately ten billion nerve cells, each of which, as we have seen, can generate a sizable electrical discharge. And besides its nerve cells, the brain contains about 100 billion glia cells, each of them a small biological battery. Successfully packing such an enormous number of electrical generators into an object the size of a head surely represents one of nature's outstanding feats, especially since the cells cooperate and collaborate so beautifully with one another.

We can well imagine that with so many tightly packed electrical generators simultaneously in action, some net electrical output for them all could be measured with recording devices such as those used on single cells. Indeed, the electrical output of human brains can be readily recorded in this way. These brain waves tapped off the skull of man—a most dramatic demonstration of bioelectricity—provide, as we shall see, a powerful tool for the biophysicist concerned with the way brain neurons and glia cells interact with one another. Suppose we find out how these measurements would be made in the hospital laboratory setting.

The Brain Wave Laboratory

In a part of the hospital separate from the EKG laboratory a suite of rooms will be set aside for taking brain waves from patients with suspected disorders of the central nervous system. If we were to visit this place, we would find there several small cubicles, in each of which a patient lies quietly in bed. The overhead lights are off, but in the semidarkness we make out a bundle of wires pasted to the patient's head and stretching across his bed to a small box nearby. From this box, in turn, a cable extends through a hole in the wall to the room next door, where it enters the side of an instrument about the size of a schoolteacher's desk. On top of this machine a bank of small pens swings back and forth across a strip of paper moving steadily underneath them, writing wavy lines in jet black ink. These wavy lines are the brain waves generated inside the person's head, transported by the wires to the machine and there amplified and converted into a permanent record for examination and study.

Doctors call these brain waves electroencephalograms, or for brevity the EEG. Every day thousands of EEGs are taken from people asleep and awake, relaxed and excited, solving problems and with their minds "a blank." The expert's skilled eye can tell from an EEG record whether the person is awake, half-asleep or deep in slumber, and often he can tell not only that a patient is ill but also just what his disorder may be.

The accompanying figure shows sample EEG recordings illustrating their outstanding features (Fig. 22). Each record is a graph of the voltages put out over time by the brain activity. In the sleeping brain the voltage goes up and down two or three times every second; when the same person is awake, the voltage varies not two or three times but ten times each second. By contrast to these graphs showing smooth regular waves, the brain of a person suffering an epileptic attack generates an odd pattern of alternating sharp and slow waves, a distinctive feature on the EEG of that illness.

The three records in the figure could all be seen—though at different times—in the record from one person lying quietly on a bed in the EEG cubicle. Just as his behavior changes from one moment to the next, so too

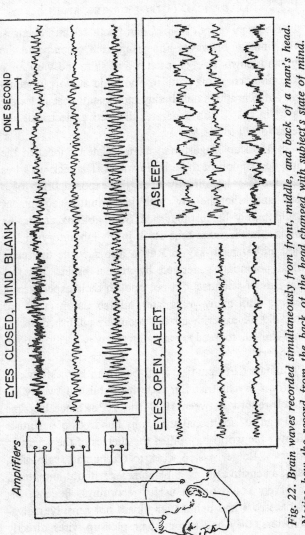

Fig. 22. *Brain waves recorded simultaneously from front, middle, and back of a man's head. Notice how the record from the back of the head changed with subject's state of mind.*

the electrical output of his brain fluctuates and changes. The number of waves appearing each second and the up and down size of each wave shift and vary in a constantly changing pattern. The brain at work organizing our sensations and bodily movements resembles the heart in that it too generates distinctive electrical currents for all to see.

In 1875 an Englishman named Caton published the first description of these brain waves. His pick-up wires (electrodes) lay directly upon the exposed brain of a dog, and what he saw with his primitive equipment could barely be distinguished from nothing at all. At just about the same time Beck in his laboratory in Poland and Danielevsky in Russia also saw the tiny electrical potentials generated by animal brains, but this last pair of scientists did not publish their experimental reports until many years later, and so Caton (who not only did the experiments but promptly published his results for all to read) generally receives credit for the discovery.

Human EEG studies were begun in earnest by the Austrian psychiatrist Berger, who published twenty research reports between 1929 and 1938. Since his time thousands of additional studies by hundreds of scientists all over the world have filled the shelves of the scientific libraries. Berger pasted wires to the human scalp, and, using a sensitive string galvanometer without amplifiers, he barely could obtain useful recordings. Because his predecessors had neither amplifiers nor sensitive galvanometers, they had to put their pick-up wires directly on the brain surface in order to record anything at all.

Nowadays a close and intimate contact with the source of voltage is not required, for modern vacuum tube amplifiers (having a voltage gain of about 10,000) make it easy to detect human or animal EEGs from outside the skull even through a very thick layer of skin and insulating bone. The currents generated by the brain traverse the bone and skin of the head and, while reduced or "attenuated" in the process, they still activate the modern devices. The amount of attenuation introduced by the skull varies between about 2 and 10, according to measurements made of the EEG voltages before and after removing the skull over a particular region.

EEG Analysis

Many physical methods are used to analyze brain waves, to modify them, and to attempt to understand their significance for brain function. Analyzing them for their frequency content is a popular and profitable approach. If you will re-examine Fig. 22 and count out the waves appearing during any one second in the various parts of the picture, you will come up with numbers like 10, 13, 2, 40. In so doing you have measured the frequency of the EEG second by second.

Now suppose you were to set out to measure the frequencies that appear during a full hour of recording rather than in the mere few seconds' segment shown in the figure. How much of the hour would be occupied with 2 per sec activity and how much with 10 per sec?

One could answer these questions by using a ruler to measure off the record second by second, laboriously counting the waves one by one as they appear in each second. Since each hour contains 3600 seconds, you would end up with that many determinations of the frequencies present. You also would be rather tired of the whole affair and convinced that a machine capable of making the analysis automatically would be a definite boon to mankind.

Such machines, called frequency analyzers, do exist. They perform their operations electronically. A mechanical analogy to the way they work is the sieve. Suppose you faced the problem of separating a basketful of large and small pebbles into collections of uniform size. You might pick each pebble up, measure it, and toss it into the pile correct for its size. An easier way would be to pour the basketful into a sieve having a particularly sized small hole; all pebbles smaller than the hole size would fall through. The ones that didn't would then be poured onto a sieve with slightly larger holes, and all stones smaller than the new hole size and larger than the first would drop through. Repetition of this process with sieves containing progressively larger holes would quickly and easily distribute the jumble of pebbles into separate piles each containing only pebbles of a uniform size.

An electronic frequency analyzer for brain wave analysis contains a series of sharply tuned filters each of which passes a narrow frequency band just as each sieve has holes that pass a certain stone size. The electrical energy passed through each electronic filter is col-

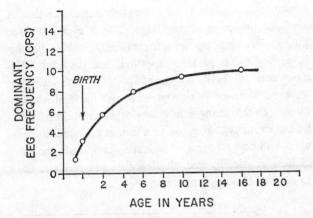

Fig. 23. Graph based on EEG measurements from hundreds of young people. Dominant EEG frequency rises in an orderly manner as children grow and develop.

lected in a condenser; from time to time the charge on each condenser is measured, and thus the amount of brain wave energy in each frequency band can be estimated.

Application of these frequency-analysis techniques reveals many fundamental facts about brain waves. Fig. 23 shows, for instance, that the dominant frequency—that is, the one most often seen in the waking brain wave of a person at rest—depends very much on age. Small children show frequencies around 3 or 5 cycles per sec, while in adults frequencies around 10 per sec (8 to 12) dominate. From such studies we know that the EEG first appears about three months before birth, with very low voltage waves at 1 to 3 cycles per sec being generated by the incompletely developed brain.

A month or so later the EEG closely resembles that of newborn babies in having large, 2 to 5 cycles per sec waves. Growing up and increasingly stable, higher-frequency EEGs go along together, and the adult EEG characteristics finally appear at about the 17th year. The attempts to relate this progressive rise in dominant frequency to the changes in behavior, interests, and intellectual capacity that go on as children change into teenagers and beyond form a fascinating chapter in the story of how physicians and physiologists use physical tools to unravel biological processes.

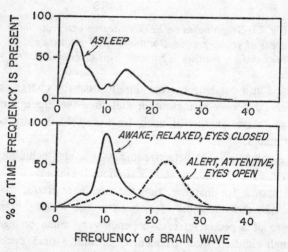

Fig. 24. Frequency analysis of the EEG generated in the back of the head. If 15-minute strips of records like those shown in Fig. 22 were passed through the analyzer, frequency distributions like those shown here would characterize sleeping, waking, and attentive periods.

The frequency analysis on several minutes of brain waves from a subject in a particular psychological state can show characteristic and rather stable features. Fig. 24 shows, for instance, the frequency distributions one would see in a person who, during the recording, was relaxed but awake, alert and attentive, and asleep. When awake, frequencies around 10 per sec are present almost continuously; this normal rhythm is called the alpha rhythm of the EEG. Despite the predominance of the alpha rhythm, however, frequencies around 6 cycles per sec (called theta) and 20 to 25 (beta) also occasionally turn up. The frequencies when alert are mostly in the beta range; animals like cats and monkeys, as well as man, show mostly beta frequencies in states of attention, problem-solving and the like. The sleep record analyzed when asleep shows the 1 to 5 cycle range (delta waves) and the 13 cycles per sec (sleep spindle) frequencies that normal brains emit during a spell of moderately deep sleep.

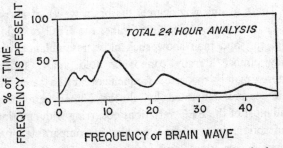

Fig. 25. A brain-wave frequency analyzer, if applied to a total 24-hour EEG sample, would show brain generating a distribution of frequencies resembling this.

Fig. 25 is an imaginary analysis of a brain wave recorded from a normal person throughout a 24-hour period. One must imagine what such a record would look like, for nobody, to my knowledge, has actually gone through a full day of work, rest, study, and sleep with wires running from his scalp to an EEG recorder. Someone may eventually spend such a day under investigation with a portable transistor EEG amplifier feeding a small transmitter that sends his brain activity to a not-too-distant recording device. When he does, the EEG analysis will doubtless show, as in Fig. 25, the various prominent frequency bands already discussed and perhaps also the extra hump in the region of 40 or 50 cycles per sec (gamma), which some experts consider to be merely higher frequency beta waves that appear in excitement and alertness.

The EEG of Animals and Man

To an astonishing degree, the brain waves of all animals look alike. Asleep or awake, the EEG of guinea pig, cat, and man show such close resemblances that they almost literally cannot be told apart. Indeed, approximately the same frequencies at the same amplitudes are generated by all the higher vertebrates, and most of the EEG variations occurring with emotions and actions in man show up also in comparable situations in cats, dogs, and monkeys. As far as one can judge from the EEG, therefore, the brain works similarly everywhere. Confident of the general validity of this rule, physiologists make their measurements on either animals or man. The choice often is dictated by which animal is available. Whatever can be discovered in the way of general principles on one brain will apply to all, the physiologists believe.

Actually, working with animals has both advantages and disadvantages over working with human beings. Cats or monkeys, for instance, may be prepared in the operating room with EEG pick-up wires permanently embedded within their brains so that the experimenter can examine the electrical activity occurring at one particular place over a period of weeks or months, meticulously charting its variations as the animal manages its daily business. The knowledge we have about events going on deep inside the brain has come largely from these studies. Such experiments would be incomplete unless the experimenter knows the exact position of the embedded electrode. The experimental animal is therefore put to death in a humane manner when its EEG recordings are finished, and the brain prepared for study under the microscope, procedures obviously impossible with human subjects. Uncovering certain kinds of information, therefore, practically requires the use of animals as subjects.

For this reason animals with implanted electrodes can be found "stabled" as horses once were, patiently waiting their turn to serve as subjects in EEG studies, in laboratories throughout the world. These dogs, cats, monkeys, and rats receive the best of food and the finest care, for unless their health and spirits are equal to that

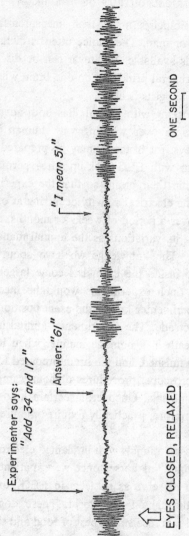

Fig. 26. What happens to the brain wave when one is mentally alerted. The 10-per-second waves disappear.

EYES CLOSED, RELAXED

Experimenter says: "Add 34 and 17"

Answer: "61"

"I mean 51"

ONE SECOND

of the best-tended pet, the experimental results are likely to be meaningless.

Among the disadvantages of using animals for EEG studies is the feeling in a certain segment of our society that animal experiments are inhumane and should be prohibited by law. People who feel this way (antivivisectionists) sometimes seriously contend that scientists working with animals are depraved and wicked men. The antivivisectionist crusade, though waning in strength at the present time, has often prevented scientific progress in the past. Fortunately for mankind, the antivivisection arguments could not prevent the spectacular march of medical science during the last thirty years— achieved largely through carefully conducted animal studies—and most people are now honestly convinced of the value and need for animal experimentation conducted by responsible investigators.

The main disadvantage in using animals rather than people for EEG studies, however, is that animals cannot talk. People easily answer even very complicated questions, but a dog or cat rarely understands what you are after even though your question may be very simple and direct. It is really a great convenience to get prompt answers to the questions you ask. Imagine duplicating on a dog, for instance, the simple EEG experiment of Fig. 26 where a person incorrectly added 34 to 17, then corrected his mistake. Answering questions involving words and numbers poses few problems for us, but for animals anything beyond the simplest manipulation of such symbols is impossible.

EEG studies with animals consequently are limited

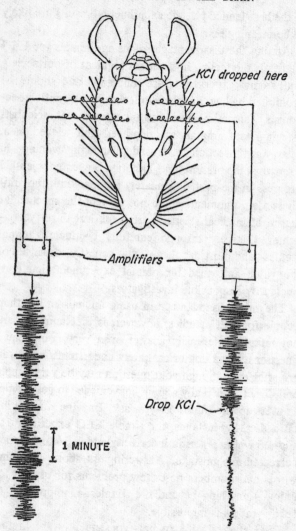

in the main to watching what happens as the subject performs a task that comes naturally to him, either because he was born that way or because he has learned it. Suppose we take for an example a study of a rat reaching into a test tube to get a bit of food. If the opening is too small for his muzzle, he reaches in with a hand, pulls the morsel out, and gobbles it up. If you watch a particular rat do this several hundred times, noting which hand he uses in each trial, you find he uses one of them far more often than the other. It seems that rats, like people, are either right- or left-handed.

The Czechoslovakian physiologist Bures demonstrated that this natural preference does not appear unless a normal EEG is present. His experiment went like this. First, he abolished the EEG waves by dropping a small quantity of KC1 solution directly on the brain surface through a hole drilled in the skull. Shortly after this KC1 hit the brain, the EEG waves disappeared (Fig. 27); after a few hours they returned to normal once more. If the hole through which he introduced KC1 lay over the left half of the brain, the EEG disappeared on that side only. Since Bures prepared both right- and left-sided holes, he thus was prepared to abolish the EEG waves for a while on either side of the brain as he chose.

A right-handed rat without brain waves in the right half of its cerebral cortex reaches into the test tube for

Fig. 27. Waves can be abolished on one side of the brain only, as in the case of this rat. The half of the body controlled by the disturbed half of the brain is abnormal until the waves return.

food in the normal way. With the EEG absent in the left half of his brain, however, the rat behaves very incompetently, rarely reaching into the test tube even though he may be hungry and has shown many times that he knows what to do to get food. Bures's experiments always turned out the same way. Whenever the EEG disappeared on the side opposite to that of the preferred hand, the rat failed. This result makes good sense when you recall that nervous control for each half of the body resides in the opposite half of the brain. Disorganizing one half of the brain should lead therefore to troubles on the opposite side of the body.

Now, since Bures showed that when the EEG disappears so does the accustomed behavior, it is only natural to suppose that something in the EEG wave tells which hand a given rat will prefer. Despite much study, however, no one has ever found any way in which the EEG of a right-handed rat differs from the EEG of a left-handed one. It may be true that the left and right halves of the rat brain generate characteristically different EEGs, but if so the point remains to be proven.

Brain Waves and Learning

When a youngster gets the idea that $2 + 2 = 4$, a change occurs somewhere, somehow, inside his head. Learning anything new must involve a reorganization among the billions of cells in the brain. However obvious this may be, the riddle of exactly what becomes reorganized, and how, remains to be solved by science.

Animals and people acquire through learning nearly everything they do. If you have a cat or dog, you realize that most of the habits he displays are peculiar to him alone. My fat and healthy cat, for instance, turns up on the back porch at breakfast and dinner time and meows piteously until someone feeds him. My brother's dog, on the other hand, dances on his hind legs to get a peanut. These animals were not born with such habits built in; they learned them. To prove this, one needs only to teach a dog some new trick, or to recall how, as a student, he himself learned new facts.

The basic pattern of every animal's behavior, including our own, is determined by such inborn drives as hunger, self-preservation, and the need to reproduce the species. For instance, the newborn baby comes fully equipped to suckle and to swallow milk, and if he did not know how to do this much, he would not be long for this world. He also comes prepared to cry loudly so people will know he needs food again. These basic patterns of behavior, and many others like them, became established through millenia of hereditary trial and error by the species.

But every individual member of a given species modifies his basic patterns to suit the world he lives in. He "learns" to act appropriately, either by putting 2 and 2 together for himself, or by having someone else do the teaching. A normal 3-year-old who toddles into the street where cars rush by would, if hit and not killed, learn through the experience to be more cautious next time. What usually happens, however, is that his mother doesn't give him an opportunity to learn by himself that automobiles are dangerous. She tells him in no uncertain terms—by a spanking if necessary—that he must not wander beyond the curb. Thus his tendency to explore and investigate new territory, a behavior pattern easily recognized in every healthy curious youngster, becomes revised through one or another kind of learning to exclude the middle of main highways.

The ability to learn is not limited, of course, to ourselves and our pets. It extends from the top to the bottom of the animal scale. Oyster and octopus, parrot and elephant—one and all form new habits as life goes on in the world they know.

Some recent EEG measurements made on the brain during learning outline the newest and, for some investigators, the most exciting field of biophysical research. Here is an example of one such EEG study pointed toward uncovering how the brain works in learning.

Suppose I set you down in a comfortable chair in a quiet, dark room. I put earphones on your ears, electrodes on your scalp, and then walk out, closing the door behind me. Alone with your reveries you relax— and your EEG shows the 10-per-sec alpha rhythm characteristic of the resting, mind-a-blank state.

From time to time I push a button outside and for a moment or so you hear a faint buzzing sound in the earphones. At first you listen to the sound—and the alpha rhythm disappears from your brain waves—but after a while you do not. When a person pays no attention to a sound, his EEG reflects his indifference by showing no change (Fig. 28).

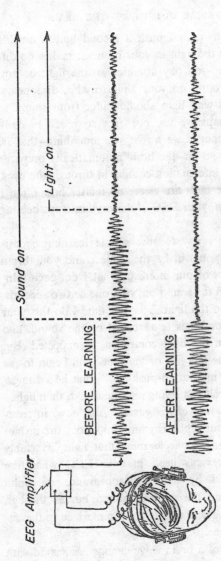

Fig. 28. EEG change in a simple learning experiment. A weak sound usually doesn't flatten the brain wave, but light always does, as the top record shows. When the subject realizes that light always follows sound, the 10-per-second brain rhythm disappears as soon as the sound comes through earphones.

From time to time I push a second button outside which turns on the light in your room. It makes no difference whether you pay attention to the light or not; every time it comes on your alpha rhythm disappears. No one knows why light should differ from sound in this way. Perhaps we use our eyes so much in daily living that whenever we *might* see something—that is, when the lights go on—the brain automatically prepares itself to accept information coming in through the eyes. In any case, the facts are clear: no matter how often I turn the light on, your EEG alpha rhythm stops beating every time.

Now we are ready for the simple learning experiment in which you will be the subject and your brain waves the object of our interest. What I do, each minute or so, is turn the sound on, wait one or two seconds, and then turn on the light. The first time I do this your alpha rhythm continues undisturbed by the sound, and disappears when the light comes on, as expected. But after I have done this five or ten times you begin to get the idea behind my button-pushing. "What he's doing," you say to yourself, "is giving me sound first, then light— I've learned the rule of his game." And now, interestingly enough, your alpha rhythm blanks out the instant the buzzer sounds. Your learning that light invariably follows sound reveals itself in your EEG when the change produced by light (disappearance of alpha rhythm) turns up the moment sound buzzes through your earphones. These events are summarized in the accompanying figure.

This instance of a brain wave change associated with

learning was first studied nearly thirty years ago. Since then scientists the world over have repeated the experiment, varied it, and invented new experiments resembling it. In Japan, Russia, France, Hungary, Canada, Uruguay, Mexico, England—you name the country, and there is a good chance at least one of its native sons has tried in the laboratory to relate the EEG to learning. In this world-wide research effort the EEG of fish, turtles, birds, cats, and many other species have been examined, and the list continues to grow every month. Scientists are leaving no stone unturned in their search for nuggets of new facts.

How many such people are at work on this problem? Any estimate is merely a guess, but probably there are no more than 500. What an infinitesimal fraction of the world's population is struggling to discover what goes on in man's brain as he learns new things! Their efforts have turned up many neat relationships showing EEG changes in learning, like the one just described, but most of the investigators freely admit only the surface of the problem has been scratched.

What went on in your brain as you read this book, learning new things? Would analysis of your EEG over the past ten minutes reveal the essential features of the learning process? No one can answer these questions. And the pitifully small group of experimenters trying to find the answers are always happy to welcome to their group any adventurous young soul who wishes to join them.

CHAPTER 7

PHYSICS, BIOLOGY, AND TIME

Time waits for no man, the old saying goes, and one might add that no man has much of an idea what would wait for him if time did do so. Our words *before* and *after, yesterday* and *tomorrow* and a host of others refer to an aspect of human experience so universal and ordinary that we scarcely give it a second thought. Yet we take for granted a *something* to which we give the name time. Everybody knows what it is—but actually when you look at it closely, this major mystery of the physical universe is a complete enigma.

To be sure, we do many things with time—besides spending, wasting, and conserving it. We build a mechanical device called a clock, chop time into pieces called hours, and thereby schedule the lives of millions of people. What is it we chop with the clock? What is this fundamental universal Time that seems to flow, steadily, relentlessly, and forever, from past to present and into future throughout the universe we know?

Philosophers try to answer this question, but the philosophers do not all agree. Most experimental scientists, by contrast, don't try, for to them questions about time seem meaningless, unnecessary, or irrelevant. Time in science is mostly merely the measurable interval between two events; give a scientist the two events and some sort of clock, and he will come up with a number expressing the interval. What more than this is there to time? We have enough difficulties already, the scientist seems to say; let people with vivid imaginations—science-fiction writers and their ilk—think of time flowing serenely, or standing still, or turning backward. We recognize, of course, the special case where moving objects approach the speed of light, since here the mathematics predict that time as we know it will slow down; and some of us even go along with the extra-special, or science-fiction case, where time moves backward for an object traveling faster than the speed of light. Except for light itself, however, almost nothing travels nearly that fast, and so in our real world time can be taken for granted as a constant, stable dimension in every relationship between objects or events.

So physicists and engineers devise methods of measuring that relationship, and the other scientists thank them kindly, use the methods in their work, and thereby discover and describe more and more subtle interrelationships among the objects they study.

We will now look at several ways in which introduction of this time dimension provides insights into nerve and muscle action—and points to new experiments still to be done.

Time and Brain Action

As we already have seen, it was Helmholtz who first measured the time required for a nerve impulse to travel from one point to another. His discovery revolutionized thinking about body function because with it nerve conduction became a measurable quantity, not some mysterious, instantaneous process no one could hope to investigate. History teaches that once something can be measured, scientists eagerly begin to measure, and Helmholtz' finding proved to be no exception. Generations of scientists have contributed—each his little bit—to what is now a substantial body of information on how long it takes for people like ourselves to do the things we do.

First of all, it has been demonstrated that nerves with small cross-section conduct impulses more slowly than do nerves with large cross-section. The bundle of sensory nerve fibers arising in the foot, say, contains thousands of individual fibers—some large, some small in diameter. Since a stimulus to that foot activates both large and small fibers, the message carried by the large ones reaches the brain earlier than those carried by the smaller ones.

A simple computation will show that this time difference is not trivial. Suppose we make the computation for the giraffe whose small and large neurons stretch some 30 feet (10 meters) from foot to brain. The small fiber conducts at—let us say—5 meters per second, while the large one conducts at—say—100 meters per second. (These conduction velocities measured on cat and man are entirely reasonable to assume for the giraffe, even though they have not yet been made on that animal, to my knowledge.) Simple arithmetic shows the fast fiber will deliver its message to the giraffe's head in about one-third of a second, whereas the slow one takes 2 full seconds to make the trip. Pinching the giraffe's ankle at a particular instant in time would therefore yield messages to the brain spread over 2 seconds, a rather long period of time. We may readily suppose that the earlier impulses produce different effects in the brain from the later ones, but the behavioral significance of such a distribution of incoming messages through time remains largely a mystery.

What holds for sensory nerves is true also for motor nerves—some have small diameters, some large. In a simple reflex act such as hand withdrawal from a hot object, therefore, the time consumed in conducting nerve impulses from the hand to the spinal cord and brain is just about matched by an equal time interval for conduction via motor nerves from spinal cord to the activated muscles. The question whether the sum of these two intervals equals the total time taken to execute a reflex act has been the subject of many experiments.

Of the reflexes studied in this connection, the knee jerk reflex has received much attention. Here is a simple and dramatic reflex response readily available for study by any experimentally minded person. All you need do is cross one leg over the other and tap it at just the right place below the knee—your foot jerks briskly for-

ward. A careful measurement comparing the instant of
the tap with the instant of foot movement would show
an interval of some 25 msec to separate them. The following table shows approximately how this 25 msec
would be divided among the several factors involved.

	Knee jerk (msec)	Eyeblink (msec)
To activate sensory nerve	0.1	1.0
Nerve conduction toward brain or spinal cord	4.0	2.0
Delay at synapses	0.9	39.0
Conduction in nerve to muscle	4.0	2.0
To get muscle activated	16.0	6.0
Total time	25.0	50.0

The knee jerk reflex-time turns out to be one of the
very shortest measurable, mainly because the incoming
sensory fiber makes direct and immediate contact with
its motor neuron, a two-neuron reflex arc being formed
thereby. The response is an automatic, built-in consequence of the stimulus.

Whenever interneurons intervene between the input
and output ones, the response loses its rigid automatic
features and the reflex time lengthens. Take for instance
the eyeblink reflex to a loud sound: the eyelid starts closing about 50 msec after the noise strikes the eardrum,
most of that time being consumed in shuttling the input
message into the proper pathways within the brain itself, as the above table demonstrates.

This switching of nerve impulses inside the brain turns
out to be a highly time-consuming process in responses
still more complex than the simple reflexes we have con-

sidered. In a reaction-time—the interval between a stimulus and the response a subject has been *told* to perform—the switching time may become very long indeed. Suppose we instruct someone to move his right foot when we flash a light in his eye. Flash of light, move right foot: this response takes about 150 msec, a 6-fold increase over the 25 msec knee jerk reflex-time, most of it accounted for as brain switching time. And if we complicate things by instructing him to move *left* foot to a sound as well as *right* foot to the light flash, the response-time to light flash increases still further and may exceed the simple reflex-time by 20-fold. What every automobile driver knows—or should know—is that something like a full second intervenes between the instant he sees the danger up ahead and the instant he jams down the brake pedal with his foot. This reaction-time, somewhat shorter in a wide-awake person—and ominously longer in a sleepy one—represents the bare minimum required for organizing his brain so that a coordinated and exact movement can be executed in the complicated situation steering a car presents to its driver.

Still other aspects of behavior come sharply into focus when we emphasize their time aspects. Do you recall the heart expert we met in the first chapter? He could talk and typewrite, two skills so common no one considers them very remarkable or unusual. Yet think for a moment of the sequence of movements and the delicate coordination required for good talking, typewriting, and the like. A moderately skillful secretary types 65 words per minute, which means (at 5 letters per word) a separate finger stroke every 0.15 second—counting the spaces. As her eyes scan the text to be copied, her brain converts the input messages into nine major categories of output ones (typists don't use the left thumb) for a total of some 90 different characters (letters of the alphabet, punctuation marks, etc.). Here is a special-purpose computer making accurate decisions—finger strokes—at a rate of over one-half million per 24 hours.

Yet only a few moments are required to convert that special-purpose computer into another very different one. Suppose our typist is busily typing when the telephone rings. She stops typing, picks up the instrument, and instantly becomes a special-purpose sound-receiving, sound-emitting computer. The sequence of speech sounds emitted by the caller evokes from her a similar string of noises—and each person knows exactly what the other has in mind. Their conversation, when you think about it, reduces basically to two strings of brain-directed muscle movements—hundreds of them every minute—each pointed solely toward making meaningful noises. As a special-purpose computer for speedily interpreting those noises and then generating appropriate ones in the form of an intelligent answer, the brains involved obviously have no equal. It is a pity we know so little about how they do this.

Just to press home how versatile the human brain-computer can be, let us suppose our typist-talker can also play the piano. Sitting before its keyboard, she now directs the very same fingers used in typing according to an entirely different set of rules. The instructions still come through her eyes but this time from notes on the printed sheet of music on the rack. Hundreds of finger

movements every minute are once again demanded—
and delivered unerringly—but her computer never mixes
finger presses appropriate for her typing with finger
movements required in her piano playing.

Speed, versatility, accuracy, small size—these features,
along with stability and modifiability, make the brain a
computer incomparably better than any other available.
To discover what physical processes yield these features
certainly presents the biophysicist with his most challenging problem, and—perhaps—with our only possible hope
for ever matching it with a mechanical device.

But let us turn from these thoughts to a somewhat
different set of biological problems where time con-
siderations also prove essential in the analysis. If the
brain's actions as a computer give the biophysicist his
most challenging questions, these other problems provide him with the most fascinating ones, for almost no
one has the slightest idea what to do to get the answers.

Physical and Biological Rhythms in Nature

To us on earth the sun-produced rhythm of light and
dark is what divides time into its most obviously different periods. Day follows night and then we start all over
again. This rhythm of light and dark, with its associated
rhythm of warmer and cooler, besides being a fundamental fact of our experience, is a cycle without which
we would probably not be alive at all. To live we must
eat, and food—even good beefsteak—ultimately comes
from plants. Experiments show plants do very poorly

when raised in a place where the light is left on twenty-four hours a day, while green plants will not grow at all, of course, with no light whatever. Hence, our very existence may well depend upon the commonplace day-night cycle generated by rotation of the earth about its own axis.

A second great rhythmical event for earth-bound creatures is the cycle of the seasons. Spring follows winter, which in turn comes after fall. The order never changes. Short winter days grow progressively longer to summer, then shorten again, and when the days begin to lengthen once more a year has passed: the earth has made its full revolution about the sun, returned to its starting place, and the seasons repeat once more.

Still a third physical rhythm comes from the tides created by the sun's and moon's gravitational pull.* This lunar cycle lasts 24.8 hours, and so it and the 24-hour day-night cycle continuously shift with respect to each other. At the seashore the lunar, or tidal, rhythm has an importance inland dwellers rarely appreciate. Periodic rise and fall of ocean water on the beach represents for many organisms a physical event just as important as the light-dark cycle, and marine plants and animals move about, change color, and show metabolic cycles in phase with both the solar (24-hour) and lunar (24.8-hour) rhythms. One cannot judge, offhand, which cycle is for them the dominant one.

This 24.8-hour lunar cycle itself goes through a 28-

* See Hermann Bondi, *The Universe at Large*, Science Study Series, Doubleday, 1960. Also see George Gamow, *Gravity*, Science Study Series, Doubleday, 1962.

day period as the moon makes a circle around the earth
and shifts before our eyes from new to full and back to
new again in the sky. Fascinating biological periods
seem tied to this cycle as well. Mating in certain sea-
living worms occurs only when the moon is full; and
some fish and turtles also lay eggs only at certain phases
of the moon. The 28-day reproductive cycle in women
looks like a rhythm that similarly could be related to
the lunar month, though if it is no one has ever figured
out just how.

Patrick Hurley tells us* that the seasonal cycle started
4.5 billion years ago, long before any organisms lived on
the earth. The other rhythms doubtless have been available to impress themselves also on all living things that
ever inhabited the earth. Have these living things actually learned over the ages to respond to these celestial
rhythms with characteristic rhythms of their own? If so,
what can be the physical basis for the rhythms by which
plants and animals regulate their lives?

Plants show such obvious seasonal rhythms it may
seem silly to mention them. In springtime trees bud out
the new leaves they will lose in the fall, and this rule
holds even for evergreens that may hold a given set of
leaves for two years. Annual plants like sweet corn
sprout, flourish, bear fruit, and die in a span of perhaps
100 spring and summer days—and this happens only
once a year where the temperature drops toward freezing in winter. Some recent experiments even show a 12-
month cycle to be displayed by certain plant seeds, which

* See Patrick M. Hurley, *How Old Is the Earth?* Science
Study Series, Doubleday, 1959.

turn out to absorb water better and to germinate and grow more readily if planted in a particular month of the year. These studies were done on dry seeds stored in the dark, part of them at −22°C, part at +55°C, with a few from each batch being removed for testing month by month. Evidently, these seeds possess physical machinery that permits them to act as a biological calendar to count off the months. What kind of biophysical calendar is this that works equally well at temperatures below and above freezing, in darkness or in light?

Animals also show dramatic rhythms. Arctic foxes turn white for winter and brown for summer. In the fall squirrels everywhere hoard piles of food at the same time the bears, woodchucks, and bats settle down for a long winter sleep. Dozens of annual cycles such as these are known to naturalists who examine animals closely. As with the seed that "knows" when to sprout, so with the animals that turn white, hoard food, or hibernate— how do they know the time has arrived for them to do whatever they do?

Research has proved that several physical factors may trigger the plant or animal response. Merely decreasing the length of daylight, for instance, causes some fur-bearing animals to form thick, heavy coats—even though it is artificial daylight to which they are exposed, and the experiment is done in March when their coats would normally be thinning out for the summer. But such physical factors—light, temperature, barometric pressure, background radiation, at least—cannot explain the animal's response entirely. He must somehow be built so as to make the response that is triggered, and a prime biophysical question centers around the mechanics of his being so constructed.

Not all animal rhythms are tied to the seasons. The beating heart we considered in Chapter 1 is an excellent example of an intrinsic rhythm of short period. Your heart has gone through its rhythmic cycle about once every second since well before your birth; when its periodic beating stops, so, unhappily, will you. Then there is breathing—once per four seconds or so. Sleeping eight hours out of twenty-four dovetails exactly with the earth's rotation cycle, and so does body temperature— lowest at 4 A.M. every day. Incidentally, the same daily temperature cycle persists in people who work at night and sleep in the daytime, and even in the man who stays awake continuously for 100 hours in an experiment. The low point of body temperature still comes at about 4 o'clock in the morning, regardless of what we do. All these instances further support the idea that clocks of some sort are built into the animal body. Not real mechanical clocks, of course, but still timekeepers that keep track of the passage of seconds, hours, months, or years.

These biological clocks offer fascinating problems to the physicist or chemist with biological interests, for their existence cannot be questioned and their mechanism is entirely unknown. Let us consider a particular instance in more detail.

The Bird's Chronometer*

Suppose we rob a starling's nest of one egg, hatch it in a laboratory, and rear the bird to maturity. The laboratory will have no window, and the artificial light by which we work will be kept turned on continuously day and night. The bird will be free to fly about as he wishes, but we will take care that he never experiences those physical rhythms impressed by movements of earth and moon upon his brothers and sisters in the outside world. No light followed by darkness, no warm sun after chilly night, etc. Whatever behavior he displays cannot be triggered by solar, lunar, or annual rhythms, for he is carefully shielded from all these, to the best of our knowledge.

Let us decide one day to put the bird to work in an experiment. First we must construct a circular cage (Fig. 29) containing 12 identical food hoppers, one at each of the clock positions. Opposite the number 12 position we install a light bulb that will remain on throughout every experiment, and into the number 12 hopper we put a plentiful supply of birdseed and other delicacies starlings enjoy. At exactly 10 minutes of 12 o'clock noon according to our wrist watch we put the bird, hungry, into the cage. He wanders about, looking into one hopper after another until finally he discovers num-

* An imaginary experiment that would work as described, according to the studies of Kramer, Hoffman, and others since 1950.

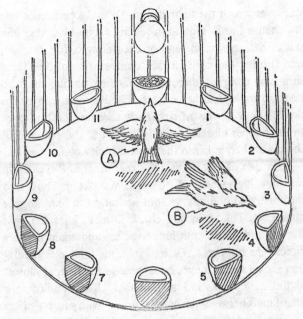

Fig. 29. Trained to find birdseed in the container below the light bulb at noon (A), bird ignores full container and goes to empty one at 4 when tested at 8 A.M.

ber 12 and food. He eats as much as he wishes until exactly 10 minutes after 12 o'clock noon by our wrist watch, at which time we take him out of the cage and terminate the experiment for that day.

The next day we again put him in the cage for 20 minutes at noon; this time he finds the food hopper more quickly and eats his fill. Day after day we repeat this procedure, and pretty soon the bird obviously has the idea: the only food hopper containing birdseed is the one over which the light shines. To make certain of this we change things around in several ways—by taking him out of the cage at the end of each minute, for instance, and turning the cage so that number 12 position faces in a new compass direction, and then putting the bird back to make another choice. Finally there can be no doubt about it: regardless of what we do, the bird goes to the hopper closest to the light almost 100 per cent of the time when put into the cage at high noon.

Now one day let us do the experiment at 8 o'clock in the morning instead of at noon. We put the bird into the cage, and he hops without hesitation to food hopper number 4. Take him out, check to make sure the light is over number 12, put him back in—and again he goes directly to hopper 4. Dozens of trials later our tabulation shows he has never once gone to the hopper closest to the light bulb, and that in fact all his choices are distributed between positions 2 and 6, with most of them at 3, 4, and 5. There can be no question about this either: at 8 o'clock in the morning the bird seems to expect food in a hopper 4 clock positions away from the one where, at 12 o'clock, he has learned it is to be found (Fig. 30). Obviously, what to us represents a minor and inconsequential change in the experimental conditions—asking the bird to make choices at 8 o'clock instead of at 12—is to the bird a major matter indeed. What would make little difference to us makes all the difference in the world to him, and understanding why this is so should give us some entirely new insights into the physics and chemistry of his brain.

To explain this experiment, we must imagine that the

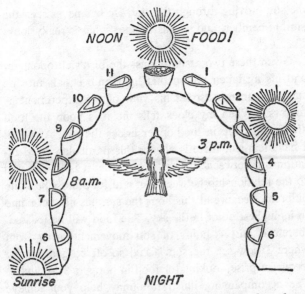

Fig. 30. If bird thinks light bulb is the sun, then the feeding place must shift position hour by hour, and sun is directly over food only at noon. At 8 A.M. the sun must lie over the empty fourth cup to the left.

bird, unlike us, has an accurate clock inside his body that tells him exactly what hour of the day it is. He has no need for a wrist watch because whenever he wishes to know the time he merely consults his own personal built-in timekeeper. Visualizing the equivalent of an accurate clock built naturally into the brain of a bird is not easy for us because we haven't one ourselves, but let's imagine it as best we can. To explain our experimental results we need to imagine in addition one more thing: that the bird thinks the light bulb is actually the sun moving through the sky. He has never seen the sun, remember, and so has no idea what it really looks like.

Given these two assumptions—the bird's chronometer and his mistaken notion that light bulb equals moving sun—we can reconstruct his view of the experiment as follows. "When my clock tells me it is noon the food always turns up in the hopper under the sun. At noon, I have learned, there is always this particular, fixed relationship between sun and food. Now it is 8 A.M. and so the relationship between sun and food must be quite different, because at this hour the sun has not yet come to its highest point in the sky. The food will be located, therefore, just 4 hours of sun movement away from where I now see the sun." And so off he goes, much to our surprise, looking for food in hoppers 3, 4, and 5. The accompanying illustration may help you achieve this bird's-eye view of the experiment (Fig. 30). If you can without hesitation name the hopper he would select when tested at 3 o'clock in the afternoon, you, too, see the problem as he sees it.

As he sees it, that is, according to the best information we now possess. The illustration, you will note, supposes the bird to point his head toward the north as he makes his computations, an assumption not considered previously. But perhaps adding this new requirement makes it neither easier nor more difficult to swallow the explanation; the entire hypothesis seems most improbable anyway. Yet no one has thus far suggested an alternate explanation that comes as close as this to explaining the observed experimental facts. For the time being, then, we may take it for granted from the various studies on starlings and several other species that birds automatically keep accurate track of local clock time and compare the sun's position with it to see if they agree.

Relating the sun's position to local clock time should perhaps not be too difficult to comprehend. We all know that a woodsman or farmer estimates time of day with fair accuracy merely by noting how high the sun hangs in the sky. Even knowing what time it *ought* to be is a skill people possess in a most rudimentary form. In this modern age New Yorkers who at home regularly awaken around 7 A.M. often discover, on being transported by jet to California, that they open their eyes the next day wide awake and ready to get dressed at 3 A.M. local time. This disconcerting experience, which fortunately tends to disappear after a few days in the new place, suggests that man can indeed carry the knowledge of his customary local time stamped into himself in some manner. Until recently it would have been difficult, or impossible, to test whether he possessed this ability for, unlike a bird, man's limited mobility tied him closely to one spot on the earth's surface—where local time and sun time must always agree. He could not transport himself hundreds of miles away whenever the mood seized him, as could the birds, to a place where sun time would disagree with local time at home. We therefore faced the problem of navigating rapidly over long distances very late in our history. With the bird it has always been the other way around.

If you grant that the California experience of the

early-rising New Yorker demonstrates a built-in time sense (at least to the extent of knowing when we are actually far away from home), a relatively simple extrapolation of the idea will account for how a bird like the pigeon, with an exquisitely delicate and precise chronometer, performs the seeming miracle of homing from a distance of several hundreds of miles over terrain he never saw before. Here, for instance, is the explanation for bird-homing that some of today's experts give. The bird at home naturally and unconsciously sets his chronometer accurately to the sun's position. He synchronizes his inner clock, minute by minute, to the place in the sky taken by the sun as it swings through its great arc from the eastern horizon (dawn) to its highest point (noon) and finally down to its sunset position. The bird thus comes to "know" exactly where the sun "ought" to be every minute of the day at home. He even makes the day-to-day adjustments required by the seasons.

If one day he flies directly south on a foraging expedition, he discovers, at noon on his chronometer, that the sun reaches its zenith—that is, it stops rising and starts falling—at exactly the correct time, but the point it reaches in the sky is a bit *higher* than at home. If on another day he finds himself several miles due west of home at home-time noon, he notices that the sun has not yet quite reached its zenith, but when it finally does get there, it reaches its expected height above the horizon.

Now suppose one day we transport this bird, blindfolded, to a release point southwest of his home, freeing him exactly at noon by his chronometer. He promptly consults the sun, finding it not yet at its zenith (so he must fly east), and when it does get there it hangs too high in the sky (hence he must fly north). So he sets off in a generally northeasterly direction and, if we have not taken him too far, he soon enters familiar territory and guides himself over the last miles using visual landmarks. His mysterious homing, then, reduces to the ability to keep time accurately (the chronometer) combined with close observation of the sun's position and a certain amount of experience away from home.

Anyone who has sailed the ocean knows that exactly these ingredients make navigation possible for man. Every ship's captain preciously guards his chronometer, which is a clock telling him exactly what time it is at Greenwich, England. At noon he breaks out his sextant to determine the exact moment the sun reaches its zenith, and its exact height above the northern horizon when it does so. Noon local time compared to noon Greenwich time gives his position east or west, while sun's angle above the horizon yields the estimate of position on the north-south axis. The two together fix uniquely the earthly position of the observer. And while this method guides the ship day by day toward a desired port across a sea without landmarks, the captain, once in sight of land, proceeds to moor his ship at the dock using his eyes alone.

Now what could be the nature of the bird's chronometer? Can the principles here at work be the same as for the seed that knows when to sprout, the bat about to hibernate, and the heart repeating its beat? In what terms do we express these principles: chemistry, physics, or what? At the present time no one knows how these questions can best be answered. But since science deals with question-answering, we can be sure that many people are hard at work right now searching for the answer to this one.

Conclusion

Men and women are hard at work searching for the physical basis of the bird's chronometer and his homing behavior . . . diligently hunting for the brain events underlying learning . . . the reason a newborn puppy breathes . . . why my pet cat meows when hungry . . . the source of the IPSPs that enable me to keep my finger on the hot radiator—if I will it—instead of jerking it reflexly away. Most of them believe that properly applying the available techniques of physics and chemistry eventually will lead us to understand the physical principles through which brain cells drive animals to do the many things they do. What each hopes for most is that he will have the wit and wisdom to figure out which of the available techniques to apply, and exactly where to apply it. Let's face it: we are still pitifully ignorant about how the brain works.

But when one remembers that Galvani only 175 years ago knew absolutely nothing at all about how nerves and muscles work, our present situation may not appear so bleak. What we now recognize as fact, however little it may be, is a body of knowledge vastly greater than anything Galvani ever imagined or dreamed. And if Galvani, wise as he was, seems ignorant compared to us, how ignorant we will appear to our descendants a century hence!

Perhaps the biggest forward step between now and then will come from those experiments in which the brain is studied not as a collection of nerves alone, but as a community of nerve cells and glia cells snugly tucked away inside the skull. Do you remember those glia cells in Figs. 14 and 15? The electron microscope sees them wherever it sees nerve cells. Yet most of this book (which has tried to reflect the best modern thinking) deals with nerve and muscle action as if these glia cells were not there. But they are there, and physiologists at the present time are beginning to wonder what they do.

No experiment rules out the possibility that these glia cells are involved in learning, in causing a puppy to breathe, and in generating my IPSPs. Along with the neurons they surround, these glia cells might even have an important role in generating the EEG—nobody has settled this matter one way or the other. The glia cells outnumber the nerve cells in a brain like our own 10 to 1—and yet you find no experiment on the glia cells in this book because there are almost none to tell about.

As we have seen, the biophysics of nerve and muscle grew and developed because people asked the right questions at the right time. Until recently we were not ready for the question, "What does the other side of the moon look like," because there was no way to answer it. But now, as we prepare to send someone up there to look, confident he will return to tell us what he saw, the question has become a good one. So it is with the question, "Do glia cells and nerve cells *together* make behavior possible?" Biophysicists in various parts of the world have begun to sharpen up their tools, and so this question too has become a good one.

INDEX

(Page numbers given in italics indicate illustrations)

SCIENCE STUDY SERIES